2 MILLION
YEARS OF
THE FOOD
INDUSTRY

NESTLÉ

Nestlé's wish, in publishing the book ''2 Million Years of the Food Industry'', is to offer a reminder, in its 125th Anniversary year, that as a company, its activities first and foremost respond to a basic human need: food.

The authors have chosen to start their story of the food industry with the use of the first stone tools some two million years ago.

Past, present, future... the same questions arise: how to prepare and preserve raw materials produced on land and sea, and how to transform these into food products.

Technical progress over the years has opened up the possibility not only to develop novel preservation processes for food, but also to take into account new criteria linked to the needs and desires of today's consumer. I would mention, as examples, the need for healthy foods, increased convenience, and an ever-growing insistence on flavour and quality.

In celebrating its 125 years of activity, our company is honoured to have been able to add an important contribution towards establishing the food industry in the world as we know it today.

Helmut O. Maucher
CHAIRMAN OF THE BOARD AND CHIEF EXECUTIVE OFFICER
NESTLÉ S.A.

2 million years of the food industry

We gathered and collected. We hunted, fished, herded and farmed, in our constant search to refine our diet. All through the ages, this hunger for progress accompanied our efforts, and it is still with us today. Our basic human need to eat drove us to improve our food, to preserve, store and trade in it. The seed of the food industry slowly germinated.

The story of our modern food industry takes us back at least two million years. It describes the domestication and management of foods, as it follows mankind's long and often hungry march across the face of the planet.

But we can begin even further back, about sixty million years ago. We... were already there. Or at least, our distant forebears or their parents were. Tree dwelling creatures who, in a long but direct process of inheritance, became man.

In those days, we were just animals among the other animals, except maybe more cunning than most of them. But was this always enough? The fight for our daily bread often meant wresting it from our competitors. And at the same time taking care not to end up on the breakfast table of other beasts wilder than ourselves.

Daily life was certainly far from the romantic image of the Garden of Eden. In today's relative comfort, it is difficult to imagine just how hostile our surroundings really were. Yet, for our remote ancestors, life must have been an endless tightrope, with survival on one side and starvation on the other. Given the circumstances, were we really at fault when we picked the fruit from the tree of knowledge? And are we wrong to have kept the taste for it ever since?

Our first real breakthrough was simple. We began to eat with our fingers. This conscious or instinctive act gave us other advantages. We dug out grubs and roots. We separated and selected what we ate. And we prepared our first rough and ready feasts in a more sophisticated manner than the other animals around us. Our hands obeyed the ever more complex orders given out by our slowly developing brains. And when we learned how to talk to each other, our skills increased even further.

About fifty six million years ago, as the hominid *Australopithecus*, we lived on small game and fish, along with what we gathered in the forests. Then in the Lower Paleolithic Age, we began to use stones as our first tools for hunting and for preparing our food. We improved these by using other stones to chip them into particular shapes. This was about two million years ago, and our story of the food industry could begin. By then, we had been promoted to the status of *Homo habilis*. A title we well deserved.

We discovered new horizons in our efforts towards better eating. We felt hungry, we ate. We felt hungry, we ate again... repeating our experiments over and over, and storing in our still evolving brains an ever growing wealth of know-how and knowledge on our foods.

We improved our methods and their efficiency, and soon viewed with pride our rise to the status of *Homo erectus*. We were ready for the great leap forward. The taming of fire.

After that, there was no looking back. The spark of genius that kindled our brains some 800 000 years ago lit up our future and set us apart once and for all from the rest of the animal kingdom.

More than 770 000 years passed from the day we domesticated fire to inventing the first oven: a hole in the ground heated with a bed of hot stones. During this long trek, we graduated from *Homo erectus*, first to *Homo sapiens*, then to Neanderthal Man. Almost yesterday it would seem, we became Cro-Magnon Man, on our way to what we are today. But before our story evolves into modern times, let us take the train of history back to our station of *Homo erectus*. We are finally the masters of fire. All sorts of possibilities are now within our reach. To begin with, a new sense of power, both reassuring and protective. And then, the social aspect. The evenings of yore spent in the warmth of the fireside, when human relations became richer and more organized. Our new found communal spirit meant that we ate better. Our survival was less threatened, and our numbers grew. We even dared to challenge the bigger game, and to pursue our prey farther and farther afield, as from *Homo erectus*, we became *sapiens*.

Fire opened our eyes, and also our stomachs, to new experiences. We began to smoke and dry meat and fish to preserve them, as we pursued our discovery of the world, and the thousand and one ways of avoiding its dangers. We changed physically and psychologically. Our jaws became weaker and our brains more powerful. We acquired the taste for cooked food, and the regional food habits and customs we find today began to emerge.

We now excelled as mighty hunters, and as Cro-Magnon Men of 40 000 years ago, we relished a well roasted hunk of wooly mammoth, with an aroma that made the mouth water.

Wildlife was the source of everything. Food, clothing, tools, the basic elements of comfort and of ornament. More than that, it inspired our primitive graffiti, as naissant artists sharpened their skills on cave walls. Our art called on the mysteries of magic, as we invented techniques and devised tricks and traps to capture animals more effectively. Over 20 000 years ago, we brought our food closer to the plate by animal breeding! Here, we started modestly, first keeping deer and antelope in captivity, and then sheep. As we emerged from the Upper Paleolithic Age and into the Mesolithic, the dog had already become man's best friend, and with its help, we really began to rear animals for food.

By now, the Christian era was only about nine thousand years ahead, and we were beginning to settle on the land in small communities. Around this time, the goat was domesticated, followed 2000 years later by the auroch cattle. Everywhere, hunting was slowly being replaced by livestock breeding. Each millennium brought new additions: the ox, the buffalo, the yak, the horse, the goose, the chicken, the duck.

We domesticated the first edible roots by transplanting them. In these first stages of the Holocene period, grazing and ploughing developed side by side, as temperatures stabilized after a series of harsh climatic changes.

In Nature's wilderness, wild grasses grew. Some of these had fragile stems which would break in the wind under the weight of the ripening head. This meant that the wild corn, or einkorn, resowed itself year after year and became more and more prolific. It only needed to be gathered in. The last of the hunters began to settle in these regions that were naturally rich in wild cereals.

Then, one day, we started to cultivate cereal crops. This meant more work, but we were probably driven to it by our exasperation with the unpredictable winds which often dispersed the seeds before they were ripe, leaving only a handful of ears behind. We slowly realized that the ones left behind were those with the less fragile stems. After harvesting and replanting, they gave us new cereal types which were truly wind resistant. The agricultural revolution was underway.

We harvested our crops with stone sickles 8000 years ago. We stored the grain in holes in the ground with clay floors, like those in the Fayoum in Egypt. Thus, we planned for our survival during the lean season.

The voyages we made during our migrations and wars carried cereals all around the known world. We became property owners, possessing fields and herds. Trade was also beginning to take shape. Raw food materials, techniques and products were imported, exported and distributed. The scene was set for the modern food industry to make its triumphal entry on the stage of history.

As the waters of time had flowed under the bridges of evolution, we had patiently learned the techniques of the kitchen: how to grill, to smoke, to cook over hot stones. We had also created cooking utensils, invented the oven, and discovered hot water. ''Haute cuisine'' no longer held any secrets.

We used the flour we got from cereals to make gruels. Some of these fermented, certainly by an accident of nature, but we cooked them anyway to give our first raised bread. Using more water in our gruels, we brewed our first draughts of beer to give us fresh encouragement in our labours.

Our ever growing empirical knowledge enabled us to transform other raw materials into more elaborate products. We learned how to extract sugar and how to press fruit juices. We turned honey into mead and milk into cheese, and we transformed the grape and the olive into wine and oil.

Our treasury of fine foods continued to grow, and we had to discover how to preserve and store them. We first used fire, ice and salt, and then learned how to keep our food in jars of oil, honey, wine or alcohol. These ancestral processes still form the basis of food preservation today.

Almost up to modern times, we often had no choice other than to satisfy our hunger with the foods nature provided on our doorstep. But eating the same food every day was boring. So when we had the chance, we offered ourselves tasty treats. These soon became indispensable, and from remote horizons, luxury invaded our kitchens in the form of spices, coffee, tea and chocolate.

Today, we can savour the luxury of our two million year story of the food industry. So without further ado, on with the main course...

Contents

Today...

Primitive tools have led to sophisticated machines, and farming has become a science in response to the food needs of the planet.

Fire's most important contribution to modern industry was turning water into steam to drive the wheels of the industrial revolution.

Water, essential to all life, is the only food permanently available in modern kitchens, at the turn of a tap.

Each new generation of domestic and industrial ovens is a sign of our technological evolution. Yet, apart from the microwave oven, today's cooking methods were all invented in history or even prehistory.

Contents

The long march of cereals

Selective plant breeding has vastly increased production of cereals which form the basis of our food supply. Processed industrially into food products or ingredients, they are also valuable as animal feed for meat and milk production.

Horns and hooves, shells and fins

Only about twenty species of the animal kingdom are regularly bred for food, whereas we eat hundreds of species of fish. Most fish are still caught by trawling the seas, although we often cultivate shellfish in underwater prairies.

A vegetarian's paradise

Fruits and vegetables, like cereals, concentrate solar energy in a readily digestible form. They were among the first foods preserved in cans, and are processed even when they are sold fresh.

Contents

Delicatessen

Spices, coffee, tea and cocoa were once the meat of kings, worth more than their weight in gold. Today, they have joined the more common food products on supermarket shelves.

The essential ingredients

Some raw food materials can be eaten straight from the farm or orchard. Others must first be refined to separate the edible from the inedible parts, or to give more stable food ingredients.

The ferments of progress

Fermentation is one of the oldest food processing methods. It is a low-energy means of preserving perishable foods like meat, milk and fish, and is widely used today, both for large scale production and in small cottage industries.

The spirit of the still

Distilling refines low-alcohol beverages by extracting their ''spirit''. One of the early reasons for commercial distilling was to cut down weight for sea transport.

The instinct
of preservation

Foods are preserved by stopping growth of microbes which spoil them. From the earliest drying processes to modern fridges which freeze the freshness in, preservation has been vital in ensuring food supplies all year round, and in offering greater convenience.

Out of the ordinary

Optimized production and processing has made food safer and more plentiful than it has ever been, and has reduced food costs as a part of the total family budget. This in itself is an extraordinary performance.

Past, present or future, the same questions recur. How to get enough good, safe food, with a minimum of effort? Throughout its long history, the food industry has never been better placed to answer these questions...

The tools
of the trade

Our distant African ancestors, hominid *Australopithecus*, lived naked. They ate roots, leaves and fruits provided by nature, along with insects and fish they caught by hand.

As they evolved, they acquired the taste for meat, which gave them strength and courage. Mankind made his debut among these "refined" creatures. To be more precise, *Homo habilis* made his debut. In response to our hostile surroundings, we invented tools as extensions of our hands. With these, we could even cut up our food. The name of *habilis* was well deserved. With simple sticks and stones, we set to work, and began transforming the world. Soon, we were using pieces of quartz or broken flint, then stones with special shapes. Primitive, perhaps. But so efficient. And thus it was, some two million years ago, that we started to lay the foundations of the food industry.

At the time of our first ancestors, each of us hunted, fished and gathered our own food for immediate consumption. Along the road of evolution, our lifestyle has changed drastically, and still continues to change.

Every year, fewer and fewer of us produce our own food. In today's industrialized nations, only three percent of the working population farm or fish. In some developing countries, as many as eighty percent still work in food production, but the trend is the same. We are happy to leave farming and fishing in the hands of fewer and fewer experts, while we, in turn, specialize in other trades and professions. The whole food industry has gradually emerged as a natural part of this evolution in specialization. Not only farmers and fishermen, but also agronomists, food processors, distributors, retailers, manufacturers of kitchen appliances... All of them contributing the specific tools of their trades to the chain which carries food from the fields and oceans to our tables.

On this stone, we build our future

The day *Homo habilis* picked up tools to conquer the world, mankind took a conscious step along the path of progress.

We discovered how to make the best use of stones with a natural cutting edge. Then, we began to create tools, and used these to make life easier. This set us further and further apart from the animals.

We could use flint for almost anything: striking, smashing, crushing, cutting, skinning. In fact, all of the techniques we needed to survive and to feed ourselves. These were handed down from one generation to the next, each generation adding new knowledge and experience. The dull edges of the first worked stones gradually became sharper. We learned how to make more specialized tools, better adapted to our hands: scrapers, axes, knives, spikes... Lifting our eyes to the stars, we might have imagined a day more than a million years ahead. The day when we would have at our fingertips the perfect mastery to make the precise tool to fit each job.

Stone by stone, we built our future.

In the early days of science, fire, air, earth and water were seen as the basic building blocks of all matter.

The 6th to the 4th centuries BC in Greece saw an explosion in knowledge. Among the many famous scholars, Aristotle's works on nature and man created the science of biology, and laid the foundations for most of the sciences we teach today. The Romans applied science to the machines of war, but also in public hygiene, including sewers and socialized medicine. Arab civilizations specialized in translations, and a library of over 500 000 scientific books already existed in Islamic Spain more than 1000 years ago. International traders in silks and spices, and explorers like Marco Polo, united the Mediterranean with the China Seas, so that by the 13th century, Occidental and Oriental sciences had begun to exchange ideas. In the 15th century, Leonardo da Vinci linked the arts and the sciences in a Renaissance discovery of man and nature. Columbus returned from the New World with new animals and plants. Then Galileo explained the solar system, and Newton described the laws of motion.

Among these learned discoveries, common mortals continued to pass on their knowledge of foods, from father to son on the farm and from mother to daughter in the kitchen. Today, this "common knowledge" of the people has become food science, the oldest science in the world, and one of the cornerstones on which all human progress is founded.

The cave dweller

Armed with shaped stones fastened to handles of bone or wood, *Homo habilis* became a true hunter. We began to hunt in groups, where we combined forces, courage and experience to overcome strong and ferocious beasts. Whilst for smaller game, we set traps on the ground or in streams.

We knew how to cut up our prey, how to separate bones, sinews and skin, and how to use of all of them. Cutting the meat into pieces made it easier to carry back to our camp to feed the rest of the tribe. We ate our meat raw, as we did with all our other foods. This involved taking a hunk of meat, gripping a part of it between our powerful jaws, and cutting off a bite-sized piece with a sharp flint. The etiquette of the table was born.

We began to store our food. We stocked our meat, along with grains and roots, in holes in the ground, something like today's silos. Or in cool, underground caves, where the food lasted longer. We had already noticed that heat and cold had different effects on our foods, but generally speaking, we left such things to nature. We had no choice, because for a long time to come, we had no means to control it.

In the 17th century, Vossius, the Dutch philosopher, estimated the world population to be 545 million.

Looking further back in history through wars, famines and plagues, we can only guess how many of our ancestors walked the forests and plains of Africa one million years ago. There were probably about 100 thousand of them. If we still lived like they did, depending on nature for our food, there would only be enough to eat on the whole surface of the planet for 10 million of us. Scarcely the population of a large, modern city! Yet, each one of us needs about three quarters of a ton of food every year, and about the same amount of fresh water. In other words, every 18 to 21 days, we each eat and drink our own weight! And the number of mouths to feed in the world continues to increase faster than ever before. Five billion today, to six billion by the year 2000, and over ten billion by 2050! These United Nations estimates of global population bring home the magnitude of the challenge to agriculture worldwide. A challenge which is double edged. For while parts of the planet threatened with starvation still ask, ''How can we grow more to eat?'', other parts are beginning to question the environmental effects of the constant, but necessary increase in food production.

A flash of insight

We survived for more than a million years with flint tools for our crafts, and with our artfulness as the key to all progress. We changed physically, with a broad nose, a receding forehead, a heaviness around the eyes, and a strong jaw with a weak chin. In the mould of modern man, we rose to the occasion, and walked upright. As *Homo erectus*.

We migrated out of the tropics, following the wildlife as it fled the droughts. We discovered the temperate zones, and then, at the beginning of the Pleistocene period, we felt the bitter cold of the Great Ice Age in our bones. Heat was at the other extreme, and we already knew what it was, long before we conquered our fear of fire.

How exactly did we become masters of fire? We can never know. No doubt we summoned up our courage over thousands of years. Until one day, between 800 000 and 500 000 BC, one of our *Homo erectus* ancestors approached the flame, and dared to pick up a burning firebrand.

This was our first flash of insight.

From its discovery, fire was a revolutionary source of power. But the real breakthrough was our ability to control it.

Fire! Along with air, earth, water! Of these, air had always fanned the flames of fire. Earth had yielded ores, which together with fire had given iron and bronze. Only water was missing. Until the 18th century, when water was added to fire! Not to extinguish it, as had always been the case in the past, but to create a new mechanical power. Steam! Iron and steam united the four elements of the ancient philosophers, and sparked off the industrial revolution. Diesel's internal combustion engine invented in 1882, followed by Tesla's electric motor in 1888, have since added another dimension in controlled power. And completing the energy orbit, the sun has recently been rediscovered as the ultimate source of power, including the biological power naturally stored as solar energy in our foods. Little wonder our ancestors worshipped the fire in the sky at the heart of the solar system.

Blowing
on the embers

Tools, and then fire, were the two major events in our already long career. Domesticating fire changed our life. Heat, security, power... so many novel and reassuring sensations. Once and for all, we were no longer animals.

After our first adventures of picking up flaming twigs or glowing embers, we began to bring these back to our camp. We tended the flame with care, fanning and feeding it to keep it going. Then we learned how to rekindle fire from its dying embers, and how to bring it back to life once it was extinguished.

One day, probably by accident, we discovered that striking two flints together, or rubbing one piece of wood against another, gave us a spark. We coaxed this into a flame by blowing on it. Our early efforts to light fires would often fail, but finally, we could repeat the process whenever we wished.

Thus, about half a million years ago, we had created the hearth, and could look forward to our first hot dinners.

The industrial revolution began in the 1760s. Virtually yesterday, on the time scale of our two million year story, where 230 years are like three days in a whole lifetime, or ten seconds in the course of a day.

In 1765, the steam engine built in Scotland by James Watt really set the wheels of the industrial revolution rolling. Factory chimneys sprung up like gaunt forests against the 19th century skies of Europe. From farms and villages, peasants migrated into towns and cities, to work in the dark satanic mills, in the shipyards and on the docks, and to dig out coal from underground seams to fire the giant boilers. Living and working conditions in the rapidly growing cities were often wretched. Malnutrition was widespread. Even starvation. And the need for simple, low-cost, nutritious foods became critical. The industrial revolution had contributed to this need, but it had also created the technical means to do something about it. A little over two hundred years ago, the modern, mechanized food industry as we know it today began to emerge.

A warm hearthed welcome

Fire forged us in groups. Gathered around it, *Homo erectus* watched in wonder the bewitching dance of the flames. And in a primitive form of speech punctuated with gesticulations, we exchanged experiences in the techniques of fire and in its secrets.

Fire transformed all things. We used it to harden wood, to straighten branches or the horns of animals, to break stones and to work our flints with greater precision.

As a sign of the glory of the times, our primitive cooking methods gave way to the culinary arts.

Cooking our foods made them more digestible and nutritious. Meat was more tender, and our jaws and chewing muscles became smaller, making room for our growing brains. We began to eat better, and our life expectancy increased.

Our wide variety of tools and our mastery of fire gave us a firm base on which to build the food industry.

The most spectacular development in the food industry since mechanization is its international flavour.

Today, the only thing Italian in a tin of ravioli might be the name! It could be made in Belgium using pasta from American wheat, stuffed with Argentine beef, in a sauce of Spanish tomatoes and North African herbs — all in a German tin, filled and sealed on a British canning machine. It may then be sold anywhere in Europe, or even exported to other parts of the world. Modern food factories often make only a few food items. Even farming has become more specialized, with whole farms geared to producing a single crop or animal. This is made possible by our complex networks of roads, railways, sea and air routes, which carry the perishable, fresh food materials in bulk from farms to factories, and transport the processed food products to the most remote corners of the globe.

Much of our present day food distribution network comes from wars and armed conflicts: from working out practical solutions to get food supplies to distant troops engaged in battle. Today, we are fighting a different battle. Against deprivation, malnutrition and famine in many of the nations of the world. This is one of the challenges for the international food industry.

The source of life

Long before the dinosaurs, life emerged from the waters to dwell on dry land. Maybe this explains why, even today, our body fluids have almost the same mineral composition as sea water, and why water is still vital to life.

Pools, streams, rivers, lakes, oceans... early man could only set up camp where water was near at hand. Our first migrations followed rivers and streams and, from one watering hole to the next, we colonized the unknown. We could not change water's course to bring it to us. So wherever we went, we had to find it. In the dry regions, it was precious. Many times, we must have gratefully fallen on our knees before a shallow pool, and bowed our head to drink of its life-giving freshness. Sometimes, we must have fought to the death to protect our source of life. Water was still a long way from being on tap in our kitchens, and the centuries would pass before we would domesticate it.

We live today in a world of extremes. A world of feast and famine. Ancient ways of food production and processing still exist side by side with the most modern technology. Across our many cultures from the equator to the ice caps, we eat widely different traditional diets. Yet, there is one basic need that has united all of us throughout all ages. Water!

Water accounts for about 60% of our body weight. We depend on it for the chemical reactions that turn the food we eat into energy and body tissue. Water also feeds plants through the roots by carrying nutrients from the soil. In short, it is essential to all life on earth, to our foods as well as ourselves. So essential that food engineers still look for a good ''water hole'' close by when choosing where to build a new food factory. There is so much water that most of us take it for granted. We do not look on it as a basic part of the agro-food business. Yet, domesticating water ranks at least as high as controlling fire in the great discoveries that led to the modern food industry. Irrigation gave us higher crop yields. Municipal drinking water installations in every town brought better health and hygiene. Hydroelectricity gave us a clean source of power.

Over 2000 years ago, the Greek philosopher Thales summed it up when he stated that ''All life is water!'' In fact, nothing has changed since. Water has always been, and will remain the most universal item in the human diet.

Fetching and carrying

From the earliest times, we had to find ways of carrying water. Even if this was only for the few yards between the source and our encampment.

But we were ingenious, and made use of the gifts of nature. The broad leaves and bark from trees. Bamboo tubes. And in the Negev desert, our Neanderthal forebears used ostrich egg shells. We began to create our own recipients from the skins and bladders of animals we killed for food. We also used our skills with fire: we heated stones red hot, and used them to burn out hollows in pieces of wood to give shallow cups. Then, thousands of years later, we hit on the idea of making pottery.

Some peoples of the world still carry all the water they use in bowls, buckets, flasks. And sometimes for miles! Others have invented a variety of channels and conduits, from simple bamboo pipes, to the complex distribution networks of modern towns which bring water to taps in every kitchen.

Running water has meant convenience for society. But it is also vital for the food industry. Apart from washing and rinsing, it is often used to carry foods from one stage to the next during processing. Fresh peas, beans, carrots, can be moved easily in running water without bruising, as they journey through the food factory from the raw materials to the packaged food product ready for sale. Automatic cleaning of raw materials by ''froth flotation'' is another example. Raw peas arriving at a factory may contain stones from the field along with pieces of leaf, pod and stalk. In a stream of water, stones sink to the bottom and pieces of leaf and stem, float to the surface, leaving a layer of ''clean'' peas in the middle. This major advance in food technology solved a major problem in cleaning fruits and vegetables. But it only came along after World War II. Up to then, the whole cleaning process had to be done by hand.

All examples of the use of running water seem simple in retrospect. But most of the processes used in the food industry have to be simple to keep food costs down. This is one of the perpetual concerns of food technologists and engineers.

Water galore!

The birth of agriculture marked the beginnings of our intensive use of water, and led to the growth of the first villages.

The history of Jericho is intimately linked to water. The city started to grow more than 10 000 years ago, around a fresh water spring on a torrid plain near the Dead Sea. The citizens of Jericho used this oasis to build a collective irrigation system. The channels they dug are now filled in by the sands of time. But Jericho's spring is still active, and gives about four thousand litres of water every minute.

As villages became towns, and towns became cities, we had to face a new problem: waste water, and what to do with it.

Pure water supplies in densely populated towns and cities will be one of the major challenges in the 21st century.

Any water can be purified — even sea water — by methods like distilling, freezing, or filtration through special resins. But these methods use much energy. Fortunately, nature takes a hand. Rain, for example, is a natural purification process by distillation. An iceberg is a frozen mountain of pure water. Natural filtration through the soil and rock gives huge reservoirs deep under the earth. And some springs yield water pure enough to be bottled directly for drinking. Most urban water purification plants start with relatively clean water from a reservoir, lake, river or artesian well. This is then treated to remove sediment, and to offer a chemically and biologically safe water supply. Finally, traces of chlorine or ozone are usually added to prevent growth of bacteria.

The settlement of Moenjo Daro, north of Karachi, already had its solution to the problem of waste water over 4000 years ago.

Along its streets lined with shops, we can still see the open air drains made of brick. These were equipped with sumps, where earthenware toys have been found... no doubt lost by children of the past. Bathrooms and kitchens in the houses were equipped with internal clay pipes. Through these, water from baths, sinks and washbasins was run off directly into the drains outside. This included the water from the Great Bath, a monumental two-storey building with a pool about 12 yards long by 8 yards wide, and some 8 feet deep. The Moenjo Daro installations show the importance given to public hygiene at the time. However, they did not reappear in history until Greco-Roman times when water was put to more and more uses. As we learnt the secrets of civil engineering, we built new and more complex installations, like canals and aqueducts.

Today, supplying fresh water requires research. San Diego, in California, is a city of almost 2 million people, with an annual rainfall to provide water for only half that number. So they are trying out a purification method inspired by the one used on the space shuttles: namely water recycling.

The key to their method is natural and ingenious: they use a floating water lily which can double its growth in 24 hours. Waste water is first partially purified by removing solid sediment. It is then run into shallow lily ponds, where the rapidly growing plants use up the organic matter remaining in the water as ''fertilizer''. But there is more! Heavy metal impurities like lead, cadmium or mercury are also removed by being trapped in the hair-fine underwater roots. After the ''flower power'', an ultimate cleaning step gives water pure enough to drink. For the moment, this is simply used to keep San Diego lawns alive and well. Like any new food process, the water from this experimental ''plant'' must have the green light from the authorities before it can be recycled into the public water supply.

Looking 100 years or so into the future, we could maybe imagine replacing the ornamental lily with something we could eat. Then, we could have a fast growing source of food, along with an endless source of pure water, all at the same time!

Over the embers

One by one, we learned the inner secrets of grilled steak, and the arts of cooking gourmet dishes.

At first, we simply dropped what we wanted to cook directly on the bed of embers. After a while, we thought of gutting our small game, then skinning or plucking it before we committed it to the fire.

We used hot stones to grill meat and fish. Sometimes whole. Sometimes cut up into smaller pieces. The small pieces were convenient. To cook them, we could thread them on to sticks of green wood. Abracadabra! With two solid forked branches stuck in the ground, one on each side of the fire, we had invented spit roasting.

We toasted plants, and made them more digestible. We roasted whole grains from cereals and grasses on flat stones, and ate the kernels, liberated from their husks by the cooking.

More important, we found that the toasted grains no longer germinated. This gave us another way to preserve and store our provisions to see us through the winter.

Baking, barbecuing, boiling, braising, frying, grilling, poaching, roasting, stewing, toasting...! Today, a whole alphabet of cooking methods is used daily around the world. This proves that our ancestors must have liked cooked food, because the process of cooking is still with us.

Throughout history, any food processing technique or food product that we do not like has not survived. So in today's food industry, the question of how much people like a product is very important. Liking or disliking determines food preference and appetite. But this depends on more than how the food tastes. It also depends on how it smells, how it looks, how it feels... and even how it sounds! In fact, all of the senses are involved. More than this, there are national preferences. Coffee, for example, is consumed worldwide. Yet a blend liked in Japan may be detested in Germany, and what is hated in Italy may be a best-seller in Canada! Leading food companies know that their products are only as good as the consumer thinks they are. This is why they do research in Sensory Science, to guarantee a wide selection of foods, specifically designed to offer pleasure in eating and drinking to consumers from pole to pole.

In the ashes

We roasted, toasted and grilled over the flames and embers. Then we found that we could also use the ashes.

The fire was going out. So what? We buried our food in the bed of hot ash in its dying heart, and cooked it more slowly. Sometimes, we wrapped the food in thick leaves, as a sort of cooking pot to protect it from the direct heat. This gave us a new cooking method... stewing.

Even when the ashes were cold, we could still use them to preserve the foods hidden underneath. We did not know why, but the insects around us no longer infested our provisions, and even the vermin stayed away.

Fire, the supreme magician, still had more cards up his sleeve.

Cooking is still a form of magic, and if we watch carefully, we can learn some of the sleight of hand ourselves. The Hopi Indians of Arizona learned the trick of roasting corn in hot ashes. The Mexicans also, who soaked their corn in water mixed with fire ashes, before boiling it or making tortillas. When corn was brought across to Europe, the trick of the ashes was left behind. Europeans boiled it in fresh water, and developed a disease, called pellagra.

We now know why. The method of cooking makes the difference. Corn contains a vitamin, called niacin or nicotinic acid, the pellagra-preventing *P-P* vitamin. But in fresh corn, this is inactive. Wood ashes are alkaline, and cooking or soaking corn with ashes releases the vitamin. Boiling in fresh water does not. So does this mean we should still cook our corn in ashes? Probably not, at least, not if we eat foods like milk, eggs or potatoes. These contain almost no niacin, and yet, they also prevent pellegra. They give us another nutrient called tryptophan, and the natural chemistry of our body turns this into niacin. As with the niacin in corn, some nutrients in fresh foods are no use to us, but we can find them in other foods, or ''awaken'' them by cooking. Without a doubt, the study of these old food traditions is invaluable. It helps the food industry to make good products.

A puff of smoke

We learned to use the flame, ember and ash of fire for cooking. Even the smoke was useful.

We had already noticed that our food kept better once we had dried it. To do this, we had used the wind and the sun, but we saw that it dried even faster by the fire, especially in the cooler and wetter climates.

We can imagine the scene in the thick forests of Central Europe. We were probably trying to dry fish or meat over a fire. And as it dried, our food was smoked.

We must have realized the advantages of our new discovery, because we began to use it systematically. We hung our sometimes meagre morsels over fires of damp, resinous wood. The dense clouds of aromatic smoke changed the appearance and taste of our food, and added new flavours to our diet. Also, the food no longer attracted the flies.

Discovered accidentally, and developed by trial and error, the technique of smoking has stood the tests of time.

In fox hunting, the ''red herring'' is the traditional excuse for failing to catch the fox. Hunters claim that a red herring has been dragged across the fox's track: this destroys the scent, and the hounds follow the fish instead of the fox. A fishy tale indeed!

Following a red herring, means being on the wrong track. But not in the food industry, where one of the first illustrations of an industrial production line is provided by a 17th century engraving of an English red herring house. It shows the various stages in smoking herrings to give kippers: one group of workers is seen washing and gutting the fish; a second group is hanging the fish on wooden frames and raising these into place inside the smokehouse; a third group lowers frames of smoked fish to a final group of workers, who are packing the kippers into barrels ready for transport. This simple production line thus consists of four steps: washing and gutting, raising, lowering and packing. Each step is called a ''unit operation''.

Like the kipper factory, any modern industrial production line can be broken down into a series of unit operations. Except that as many of these as possible are now mechanized, to give automatic manufacturing processes. Automation uses a minimum of manpower and energy, and assures a maximum of industrial safety and productivity.

Getting into hot water

Cooking in hot water made our meat more tender than roasting.

At the time, we had no metal cooking pots or kettles to heat water over the fire. But we were intelligent! We heated stones, and dropped these into cold water, contained in a hollowed out wooden pan, or in a pouch made by hanging an animal skin between four poles. With our hot stones, we could even boil water, and keep it hot long enough to cook food just as efficiently as we could with fire.

We threw various odds and ends into the brew: a handful of grains, maybe a few leaves or roots, some bones and the leftovers from the meat, and let it simmer away quietly. We had created our first cup of hot soup.

What's new under the sun? We may wonder, when we see that the first immersion heater was invented in the Stone Age. Today, we have simply replaced the hot stone by an electrically heated element. In both the kitchen and in the food factory, we can now have a constant source of hot water at the flick of a switch.

We now know the difference between hard and soft water, and how to stop our hot water installations ''furring up''. But one of the main innovations in hot water technology has been energy saving by cutting down heat loss. Heat itself is a form of energy. In the same way as a hot stone can be used to heat water, the heat from waste hot water, from steam or from hot air coming out of an industrial process can be used to warm up fresh water entering the process. Even the energy given off as a heated product cools down can be recovered. In instant coffee production, for example, the hot coffee extract coming out of an industrial percolator preheats the water going into a second percolator. The installations used to recover and to feed back energy in manufacturing processes are called heat exchangers. Their general use in our present day food industry has led to huge economies in energy. This has a dual benefit. It saves valuable fuel supplies, and cuts down the cost of food products to the consumer.

The first hotplate

Over 30 000 years ago, we had the idea of digging hollows in the earth, and building our fires in them. Our primitive fireplace gave a natural protection against the wind, and prevented the embers from being scattered.

As Cro-Magnon Man, we became such expert firemasters that we also dug radial aeration ducts leading into our fireplaces. This kept the fire supplied with a draught of oxygen, which helped to burn the bones and wood we used as fuel.

Our inventiveness led to a new idea. We placed a stone in the heated pit. We grilled our food on its hot, flat surface, instead of cooking it directly in the hot embers as we had done before.

The hotplates in our 20th century kitchens are strangely like the hot stones used by the Stone Age chef. We heat them now with gas or electricity instead of wood or bones, but the principle is still the same.

Since its invention, the hotplate has always been popular, because it is simple and fast. Throughout history, it has appeared a variety of forms, such as the griddles or irons hung over fires in the Middle Ages. Today, the direct use of hotplates in large scale food processing is rare. However, they are often found in another major sector of the food industry — in restaurants, cafes and canteens. The griddle in the middle of the dining table in a Japanese restaurant, where a dextrous chef cooks meat, fish and vegetables right before our eyes, is simply one of the spectacular modern examples of this truly ancient technology.

From clay to oven

We were still nomads, living in encampments, following the tracks of game or running away from famine.

We left our holes with hot stones behind us wherever we went. It was easy to build others at every new halting place.

Sometimes, we dug our holes in clay. The sticky earth was remarkable. It hardened as it dried in the sun. We used it to build shelters and to make ornaments or "magic" statuettes. Only later, we began to use it to create domestic utensils.

Our mobile encampments became more and more fixed, and our cooking installations also. To make our holes with heated stones more permanent, we lined the bottom and the walls with the pliable clay, which became as hard as rock when we lit our first fire in it. These large, baked earthenware bowls, fixed in the earth, were the ancestors of the oven.

Early 20th century convection ovens in the home had an iron box with a door as a cooking space. They were lined with fire resistant clay brick, and directly heated by fire. Even now, similar ovens are used in many local bakeries. But in industry, food products are more often cooked in steam ovens.

The first type of steam oven was the pressure cooker, invented by Denis Papin in France in 1679. He cooked food with a small amount of water in a pan, tightly closed to hold in the pressure generated by the steam. This gave higher temperatures and faster cooking times. The Great Exhibition of London was an international trade fair held in 1851. Here, the J.H. Gamble Company presented a much larger autoclave they were using to produce canned foods. Then came the Perkins oven, heated by steam flowing through pipes. This gave a uniform heat over the whole oven, and for the first time in history, it was possible to control temperatures precisely. From the 1850s when it was first used, the Perkins oven revolutionized the baking industry. Temperature control allowed automatic operation, and this gave the same quality of baked goods day after day.

Making products of consistent quality is one of the secrets of success in the modern food industry. But this is only achieved by completely controlling all processing conditions.

The state of the art

The oven was one of the direct results of leaving behind our nomadic way of life and settling down.

We sometimes sank our ovens down into the earth and made fires above them. We also set them up in small huts with curved walls of stone and clay, like the one found on the 30 000 year old Dolni Vestonice site in Czechoslovakia. This was one of the very first ovens built above ground. It was evidently designed for magical or ritual purposes, since it was still filled with clay statuettes when it was discovered. Ceramic art had arrived. But, we still had to wait another 20 000 years before pottery vessels were made, in Japan.

In the meantime, the oven had evolved and spread. We made preshaped bricks to build our oven walls, instead of using stones and clay. Our new oven even had an aeration vent at the side, and it radically changed our cooking methods. The modern style oven, heated from the inside and with a door at the front, came along much later. Thanks to the inventive spirit of the ancient Greeks.

At their recent Jubilee Meeting, the American Institute of Food Technology voted microwave cooking as one of the TOP TEN food science innovations during their 50 year history.

Microwave technology came indirectly from research on radar during World War II. Today, it has many uses. Repairing road surfaces. Making textiles crease resistant. And... cooking. The ''microwave'' oven has no equivalent in history. Earlier ovens all worked by heating the whole cooking space. In microwave cooking, the oven itself is not heated. Heat is created directly inside the food! The microwaves make molecules in the food vibrate, and this gives a sort of ''friction'' as they rub against each other. Water is very efficiently heated by microwaves, so wet foods cook quickly, and dry foods hardly cook at all. By the year 2000, over half the homes in most industrialized countries will have microwave ovens, and in the USA, almost all the homes. This brings surprising new problems for the food industry: creating new cooking pots and dishes! Most of today's kitchen utensils were designed for traditional ovens, like the ceramic bowls and pots of our ancestors. They may not work at all with microwaves! So food companies are now developing meals where the package itself is the cooking pot. This preserves the convenience of microwaving.

Cereals in the conquest of man

As era followed era, we left the work of planting in the hand of nature. We were happy just to collect the wild plants and cereals that grew abundantly wherever the winds blew them. Two of the wild wheats were einkorn and spelt. These had fragile heads, which rapidly ripened, and were scattered by the slightest breeze. Almost impossible to harvest, the seeds replanted themselves unaided. With the sharp point and the curved filaments on the husk, they anchored themselves firmly into the earth. In fact, cereals had a much stronger natural instinct for farming than we did.

Twenty thousand years ago, thousands of years before we became farmers, the peoples on the plain of Kom Ombo in Egypt were already harvesting wild grasses season after season. Soon after, hunter-gatherers in Nubia and in the Zagros Mountains between Turkey and Persia were doing the same.

Without our help, cereals adapted and proliferated naturally in the wild. This is how they conquered man.

Cereal, comes from *Ceralia*, a celebration held every year in Ancient Rome to honour Ceres, goddess of the harvest.

Cereals now contribute about half of all food produced worldwide. Wheat, rice and corn are grown in similar amounts, and account for two thirds of all cereal crops. Wheat is the most nourishing, and is the mainstay of temperate climates: rice is the staple food of hot and wet areas: corn is used to feed both animal and man. Barley, oats and rye are also major crops, while millet and sorghum are important in dry parts of Africa and Asia where other grains will not grow. And quinoa grows well in the cold mountains of South America. Cereals changed society. Our nomadic ancestors began to settle in organized societies. As cereal farmers, they learned which seasons to plant and which to harvest. From the movements of the sun, moon and stars, they invented astronomy, and with it, a farmer's calendar and a system of arithmetic. Cereals also became a measure of length. A Royal decree in England in 1324 defined the standard inch as three barleycorns laid end to end. A century ago, the US shoe industry adopted this standard, with a size 13 shoe equal to 39 barleycorns.

The dawn of agriculture

Were cereals ever really wild? We might ask, in view of the constant effort they made to become domesticated.

The winds scattered the seeds. A few of the more robust ears were left behind. We sowed the grains, and they gave birth to more resistant grasses. These first conscious plantings marked the dawn of agriculture.

By 10 000 years ago, Jericho had grown to be a large village covering about 10 acres. Its people cultivated fields of resilient einkorn, spelt and barley, and stored their harvest in barns.

The villagers of the Fayoum in Egypt grew barley and millet. They harvested their crops with saw-toothed stone sickles, and stored the grains on straw matting in silos they dug in the ground.

Cereals are a good example of the close bond between us and our food. Most of today's varieties, including those we were planting centuries ago, could no longer survive in the wild. Indeed, they need us just as much to survive as we need them.

After the dawn of agriculture, new sorts of cereals continued to develop naturally. Cross-breeding between wild wheat and grasses produced natural genetic changes, giving wheats that were easier to farm. The two main wheats we grow today descended from wild ancestors: bread wheat, already grown 5000 years ago, and macaroni wheat from about 100 BC. In 1856, in a monastery garden at Brünn in Austria, a monk began to experiment on cross-breeding peas. This was Gregor Mendel. By 1865, he published his laws of heredity, which led to the science of genetics. Plant breeders began to control the evolution of cereals. Today, we have new varieties which are: richer in protein; more resistant to cold or drought; less vulnerable to disease; more efficient in using fertilizer; and giving a higher yield. Some even have a natural resistance to insects and pests. We have also created wheats where the natural biological clock has been turned off. Unlike their parents, production of these wheats no longer depends on the number of hours of daylight, and they are now being grown from the north to the south of the planet.

Every week of the year, a wheat crop is maturing somewhere in the world. A genuine green revolution.

Archaeologists state that agriculture started in the "fertile crescent" of the Middle East more than 10 000 years ago.

About the same time, we were cultivating corn in South America, and then rice in Southern China at least 4000 years before our time.

Wherever we happened to be the day we settled on the land, the long march of cereals had begun.

One head of wheat looks very much like another! Especially when driving across the Central Plains of North America, where the giant farms seem to go on for ever. In 1988, the USA produced an incredible 440 pounds of wheat per person. Surprisingly, wheat was not grown at all in the Americas till around 1820, as the settlers moved far enough west to find suitable earth.

Two of the most prolific varieties of wheat grown this century each came from a single head. Kanred, or Kansas Red, was selected from Crimean winter type wheat in 1906; while Blackhull came from a field of Turkey wheat in 1912. By 1917, enough of each had been produced to be distributed to farmers. By 1925, Kanred was widely grown, and from the single head selected 19 years earlier, nearly five million acres were planted in Kansas, Nebraska, Colorado, Oklahoma and Texas. Similarly, by 1929, Blackhull wheat already covered about six million acres. The number of varieties of wheat in the world increases every year, but the number farmed is always limited to a few. The best. Early in the 20th century, it took several years to grow enough seed from a single head for commercial planting. With modern methods, plant breeders can grow several plants from only one seed! And a single head of wheat today might yield enough seed for supplying farmers... in less than a year.

Through the mill

We used cereals for food long before we cultivated them. We threshed our gathered crop to free the seeds, and ate these whole, sometimes raw, sometimes roasted, along with their protective coat of bran.

We began to grind them. Or rather, to pound them into a coarse meal. The hunter-gatherers of Kom Ombo and the South American Indians used very rough grinding stones and pestles. The peoples of the Zagros mountains had millstones and mortars hollowed out in the solid rock of their caves. And 10 000 years ago, the Ancient Egyptians were already using stone roller mills.

We invented the wheel 5500 years ago, in Sumeria. After that, each new mill was more ingenious than the last. The pole-pivoted mill. Then the rotary mill, which appeared in the Middle East around 200 BC. This used a rotating crank to turn two stone discs one against the other. Milling became more and more efficient. We ground the grain finer and finer. Until the moment when two huge millstones, finely turning round and round, gave birth to flour.

Flour milling was the first food industry to be modernized. By 1776, a steam driven mill was operating near London. And in Philadelphia, Oliver Evans had set up a complete mechanized production line for milling grain into flour.

We can make flour from any cereal, and even from potatoes, peas or beans. But ''a bag of flour'', usually means a bag of wheat flour. The life story of a bag of flour begins with mature wheat. Each grain has a white kernel and a wheatgerm, both covered in three layers of bran. Grinding whole grains gives a coarse wholemeal flour. Milling away the germ and bran leaves the white kernel, and this can be ground into white flour. Wheat contains gluten, the sticky protein that gives the aerated structure to raised bread. The best flours for bread are the ''strong'' flours. These come from hard wheats which contain a lot of gluten. ''Weak'' flours are better for pastries and puddings. They come from soft wheats containing less gluten. Strong and weak flours mixed together are sold as ''all purpose'' flour, which can be made ''self-raising'' if baking powder is included.

In the days when all bread was wholemeal, the first white bread was a luxury product for the rich. Today, we like to be able to decide what we eat, so the food industry gives us a choice. Not just between white and brown bread, but of all food items.

Gruels to eat
or drink

Wheat, barley, buckwheat, maize, millet, sorghum, rice, rye. One by one, we domesticated them, crushed them, sometimes roasted them, and ground them into flour.

At first, we just mixed the flour with water and ate or drank it raw. This is the way the Indians of South America made a corn paste that they could eat or drink, depending on how much water they added. Then we hit on the idea of cooking the paste. We had invented gruel. From remote times, we made our gruels in natural cooking vessels directly over the fire. And for hundreds of generations, hot gruels were the staple food of humanity.

One civilization after another, gruels were the diet of the poor. Some gruels looked and smelled strange, like the one made from rye. They were also the food for hard times, when flour was made from anything that came to hand: beans, chestnuts, or even acorns.

Henri Nestlé was a man with a mission. To save thousands of young infants who were dying every year of malnutrition in 19th century Europe. This was a time when the industrial revolution had changed farmers into factory workers faster than it had developed the food industry to support them.

His dream! To create ''a whole food... a perfect food'' for the many starving babies. The spark! When a friend in Vevey, Switzerland came to him in 1867, and begged him to make something for an infant who could not digest fresh cow's milk and was doomed to die. The result! Henri Nestlé's ''Milk Food''. He made this by baking rusks from malted wheat flour. Then he crushed these into crumbs, and mixed them into sweetened condensed milk, to give a granular brown powder. This was the first instant infant weaning food, and the start of the baby food industry. The French Academy of Medicine welcomed Nestlé's invention, and scientists of the time claimed it was ''of the greatest significance in solving a major problem of public health''.

Cereals and milk are still a firm base for good nutrition, and in today's world of rapid change, ''Milk Food'' is still manufactured. Certainly with more modern engineering methods, but essentially the same product as 125 years ago. If we need a proof that basic food needs do not change with time, this is it!

Going crackers!

How did we begin kneading flour into dough? Probably accidentally, in trying to mix up a thick cereal porridge.

We had no skills in the baker's art, but we were willing apprentices. The first cakes were simple, maybe flat, maybe egg-shaped, depending on our inspiration. We baked them under the ashes, in the embers, and on or between hot stones. This is how the lakedwellers in Stone Age Switzerland made their wheat, millet or barley biscuits.

Unleavened cakes were baked in many cultures for rituals and ceremonies. The Jewish "matzoh", made by the Hebrews during the Exodus from Egypt, is still used today as the "bread of affliction" eaten at the Passover.

Flat breads, biscuits or crackers have been used in all sorts of culinary traditions: pita, pizza, tortilla, pancakes. We have eaten them savoury or sweet, covered with pickled fish, onions or fat, or with dried fruits or honey.

In fact, once we got started, it was all a piece of cake.

The French call it a galette, the Mexicans a tortilla, the Indians chupatty. The Scots have their bannocks, and the English something called sad cake. The Italians do not call it anything, but they use it as a base for their traditional pizzas.

We find these unsweetened cereal cakes in all countries around the world. Thick or thin, light or heavy, crunchy or rubbery… it all depends on the cereal used and the way it is cooked. They were one of the first hot fast foods. Easy to cook on a griddle or as a pancake, and needing very simple ingredients. When we baked them hard and dry, we got Swedish knackbrod and other kinds of ship's biscuits. These kept almost for ever, and took up very little space. Ideal for the traveller, apart from their reputation for being so hard that they loosened teeth. The problem of hardness was solved by new recipes and baking technology. A major sector of today's food industry now supplies a whole range of flaky crackers, crispbreads, water biscuits, savoury biscuits, wafers and crumbly thin cakes, made from all of the cereals. These have advantages for the consumer: they are ready to eat, and store well. They also have advantages for the food industry. They can be made on automated machines, and their regular shapes — oval or round, square or triangular — make them easy and inexpensive to pack and to transport. A true convenience food in every sense of the term.

Pearls from the East

We were harvesting wild rice four thousand years ago, in the fertile plains of the Yang Tse Kiang, Mekong and Ganges deltas. Rice became an aquatic plant by natural evolution, and we bred new strains through centuries of experiment and cultivation.

To grow rice, we laid out the land in horizontal terraces, and irrigated it by diverting rivers. We sowed it and transplanted it by hand, and left it in the sun to grow and ripen. Then we harvested it. Also by hand.

Rice became the staple food in most of Asia. It was introduced into Japan at the same time as the message of the Buddha, around 500 BC. From India, it reached Persia and Mesapotamia. It began to conquer the Mediterranean basin, and by the 13th century, the people of the Po valley were growing it. In the 16th century, it paid its passage to the New World in the holds of Spanish and Portuguese caravels.

Today, we can enjoy eating wild rice from Canada. But this is an impostor with a secret! In fact, it is... a wild oat.

At the International Rice Research Centre in the Philippines, agronomists have now bred rices which ripen in four months instead of six, giving three crops per year. The 1988 world harvest was 500 million tons. This corresponds to a pound of rice for each one of us on earth every two days!

We grow long grain and short grain rice. Long grain cooks light and fluffy, and short grain is more tender and sticky. They are both grown and manufactured the same way. Coarse grains called paddy rice are first obtained by threshing. These are milled to remove the tough outer husk, giving whole, brown rice. A second milling removes the bran to give white rice, which is then washed and polished. Milling partly removes the vitamins and minerals. This may be important for health if rice is our only food, as it once was for the sailors of the China sea. However, because white rice is so very widely eaten, it is often supplemented with the missing nutrients. White rice even has some advantages. It keeps longer than brown rice, and cooks faster. And finally, there is also parboiled rice which is half cooked with steam before milling. This still contains much of the original vitamins and minerals. Brown, white or parboiled! Whichever we eat, all of them are extremely digestible, nourishing and palatable.

Inca and Aztec gold

The early Peruvians and Mexicans were unaware of each other's existence. Independently, they chose to cultivate the same tiny grains which grew abundantly. Corn.

Nature helped them by selecting the most robust varieties, which spread like wildfire through the whole continent. All that remains now of the original corn is a sort of fossilized pollen. This dates back 80 000 years, and was discovered during excavations for the Mexico City underground.

Corn colonized the land from South to North. The American Indian civilizations were built on it, and looked on it as a sacred food. They ate it as a gruel, sugared and spiced, or along with vegetables, or with chocolate. The Peruvians fermented it to brew a kind of beer. The Iroquois Indians cooked the whole grains, and invented popcorn.

Then, over four centuries ago, mankind's golden legacy from the Americas made its way to Europe. This was about fifty years after Christopher Columbus first tasted it in the Bahamas.

Corn saved the Pilgrim Fathers from starvation. When they arrived aboard the Mayflower on American soil in 1621, the wheat they brought with them would not grow. Two hundred and fifty years later, corn led to the start of one of today's biggest sectors in the food industry.

Dr. John Harvey Kellog ran a health clinic in Battle Creek, Michigan. As one of his range of dry cereal health foods, he invented the cornflake. Today, these are made by first milling corn to remove the germ and bran. The white, starchy inside is then split into two halves, called grits: each grit will become a cornflake. The grits are pressure cooked in water containing sugar, salt and malt, then quickly dried in hot air until they are no longer sticky. They are flaked by squashing between heavy, smooth steel rollers, then toasted and cooled. Vitamins and minerals may be added. Flakes may also be coated with a sugar and honey mixture. This keeps out moisture, and the cornflakes stay crisp and fresh for longer. Kellogg's theory was that we need to chew dry, brittle food to keep our teeth in good shape. And with about fifty cornflakes in a spoonful, there was enough to chew over. John Harvey's product was commercialized by Will Kieth Kellogg, his brother, who started the family business in 1906. This set in motion a veritable avalanche of ready-to-eat dry breakfast cereals.

The noodle family

Who invented noodles and pastas? We will probably never know. So we can take our choice: the Chinese, Japanese, Koreans, Germans, French, Sardinians, Armenians or Italians. Few other foods have as many claims to paternity.

One thing is sure. They are easy to make. A little flour, a little water, maybe a little egg, and very little else. We have made them from many different kinds of flours, and they are part of the food traditions of many cultures: the farfels of the Jewish cuisine; the noodles, vermicelli, pretzels eaten in Germany. They have appeared as little balls rolled in the palm of the hand, like croquettes, quenelles, gnocchi. Or as couscous, made by crushing wheat. They have been stuffed with chopped meat, herbs, cheese, eggs or fish, to give cannelloni, tortellini and ravioli.

At least, this is what they are called in Italy. In Armenia or China, we find the same foods with different names.

In fact, pastas now come in all shapes and sizes, designed for all tastes and cultures. Is it really important who invented them? They are universal.

Some years ago, a British television documentary film on ''The Italian Spaghetti Harvest'' showed workers picking long sticks of spaghetti from fruit trees. Many people believed it, in spite of the date. April 1st! After all, few of us have ever seen a food production line, so we believe anything. Especially for ''foreign'' products.

In fact, spaghetti is made from a hard wheat semolina flour mixed with water or egg to give a crumbly dough. This is done under vacuum to prevent air bubbles in the finished product. The dough is squeezed through small, round nozzles, which produce a thick curtain of soft strands of spaghetti, about two metres long. Cut off at the desired length, these are dried, cooled and packed. Typical spaghetti machines work 24 hours a day, and produce one ton of spaghetti per hour. In today's shops, we find an amazing range of pastas: spaghetti, macaroni, rigatoni, corneli, spirali, taglierini, conchigliete, and many more. Each requires a different machine to give it its shape. The same crumbly doughs are used for all: water doughs give Napoli type pastas, while egg doughs, not surprisingly, give egg pastas.

The Italians tell many pasta stories. They claim that tortellini was created in the shape of the navel of Venus, by an enterprising innkeeper, who spied on her through the keyhole of her bedroom door as she was undressing. With stories like this, who could doubt the love of the Italians for their national dish.

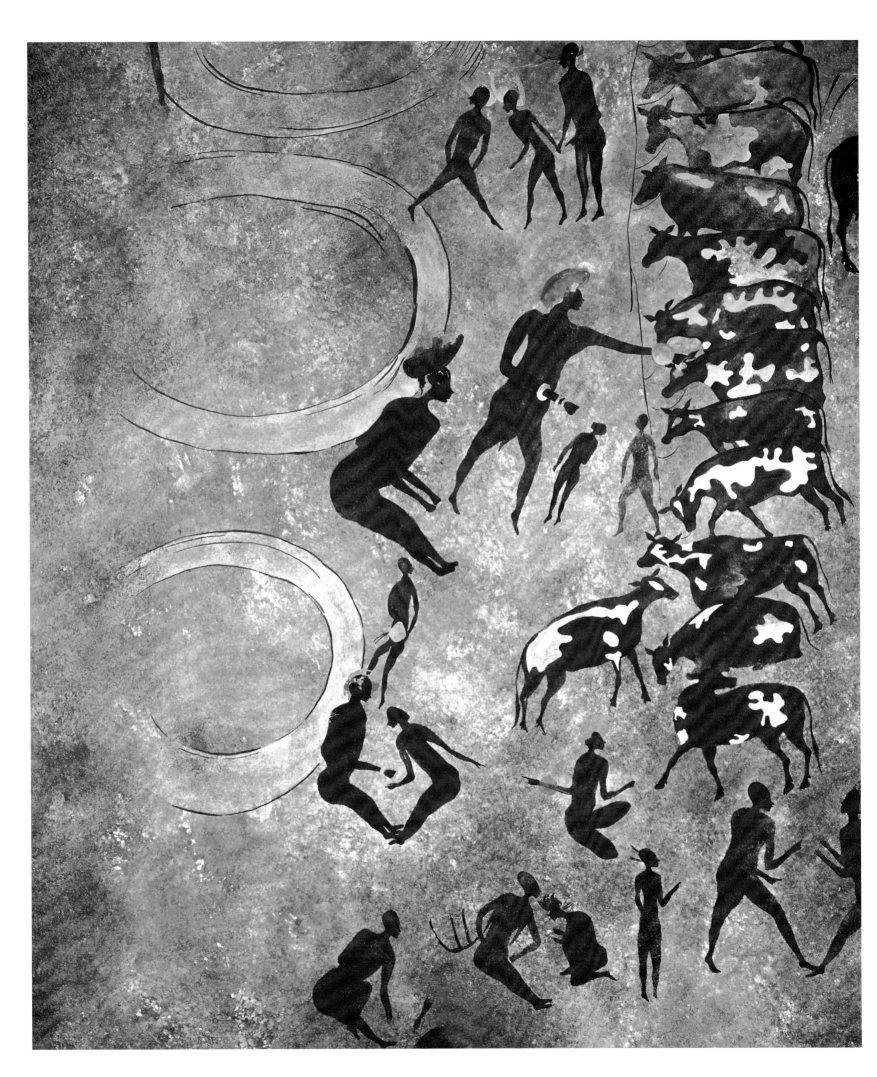

Animals in captivity

Before we became herdsmen, we spent most of our waking moments hunting and gathering. Animals gave us meat and fat for food, skins for clothing, bones or ivory or antlers to make tools and utensils, and sinew and gut for binding.

The gatherers caught the smaller game and insects. The hunters attacked the wandering herds of giant grass-eating animals. Following the herds as they migrated may explain how we crossed the Behring Strait almost 40 000 years ago to settle in the Americas.

In the high Sinai, 30 000 years ago, we had started to keep antelope and deer in enclosures. Presumably, we got tired of running after them. This was still the Cro-Magnon Age, but we had stopped behaving as crude hunters, killing as many animals as possible for immediate use. We now looked to the future. We still hunted, but we kept the females and the young animals alive to renew the herd. This was our first lesson in herd management, and laid the foundations of livestock breeding.

The first beef cattle were bred in the British Isles. They descended from the wild bull of Europe, domesticated almost 5000 years ago, and the small Celtic cattle. Hundreds of generations later, we now have the Aberdeen Angus, Herefords, Galloways and other famous beef breeds we know today.

The results of breeding are remarkable. Dairy cows which probably gave about 600 pounds of milk per year when they were first domesticated now yield over 9000 pounds. One third of all cattle bred in the world are still used as working animals. Like beef cattle, they are bred for muscle. But tough, hard muscle to pull carts and ploughs, not the finely marbled steaks for our gourmet eating. Each type of animal we farm has its own ideal diet. Pigs and chickens need a varied diet. Cattle can survive on grass, but they are also fed grain and vegetables. A famous breeder called Charles Colling fed his cattle turnips. In 1745, he set a new record with a bull weighing 3024 pounds! Even with an ideal diet, beef cattle need about 20 pounds of fodder to give one pound of meat. Pigs and chickens give about the same food value on eight pounds of fodder, and milk cows on six pounds. Hardly surprising that we generally pay more for beef than for pork or chicken.

Selective breeding could never have happened without one simple invention. The fence! It allowed us to separate the best animals from the rest of the herd.

The domesticated animal

Instead of following the herds wherever they went, we now kept them and limited their freedom. We began to specialize in herding certain species.

On the coastal plains of North Africa, between 20 000 and 10 000 BC, the Troglodytes herded the maned mouflon. Around 11 000 BC, the natives of Maladova in the Ukraine exploited reindeer. Further to the South East, there were sheep breeders in Shanidar. While in the regions which would become Italy, Switzerland, Britain and Denmark, we kept herds of deer, still wild.

The first animal to be truly domesticated seems to be the dog. At Malata in Israel, a 14 000 year old tomb contains two skeletons. The master, and his faithful hound. Then, maybe because of their herd instinct, the sheep and the goat trustingly followed us along the path of domestication – a path already trodden by about twenty other animal species before we entered the Christian era.

Gradually, smoothly, we left hunting behind, as we also stepped out, along the path of the herdsman.

By the mid 19th century, North America, Argentina, Australia and New Zealand were already producing more beef and mutton than they needed for their home markets. The excess meat was simply thrown away, and the fat turned into soap and candles.

The main problem for exporting their meat was to keep it from spoiling during sea transport through the tropics. The first real solution came 150 years ago, with corned beef factories, like the one in the town of Fray Bentos in Uruguay. Then T.S. Mort, an Australian wool broker and E.D. Nicolle, a French engineer, built the first frozen meat factory at Darling Harbour, Sydney. By 1873, they could keep mutton, lamb, beef, poultry and fish frozen for six months. The next step was refrigerated ships. In 1877, a shipment of frozen mutton left Buenos Aires on a French ship, ''La Frigorifique''. The crossing lasted six months because of a collision at sea. But the meat, frozen to $-17\,°C$, arrived at Le Havre in good condition. In 1882, two million carcasses of beef and mutton were shipped from New Zealand, and four million carcasses ten years later. The transoceanic frozen meat trade had begun. Imported meat improved the poor diets in the towns and cities of Europe a century ago. By then, we had forgotten the fears of earlier generations, who believed that eating meat would make them dim witted and stupid.

The essence of breeding

Evolution had always happened by natural selection. We now found that we could control it. We could "design" the different animals we used for food to suit our needs.

We killed the big and more aggressive males, and kept the small ones for breeding with our herds of females. From generation to generation, we produced smaller and more docile animals. They also looked different. The straight horns of the wild beasts curled round into a spiral. Ewes lost them completely. Even the viciously pointed horns of the wild auroch bulls became less dangerous.

Time passed. Some domesticated animals returned to their wild state: the deer, the gazelle, the antelope. Others almost disappeared, like the onager, which we replaced by the donkey and the horse.

During the past 10 000 years, we have changed the nature of wild animals by controlled breeding. This made it easier for us to exploit their meat, milk, hides and wool. From all of the species in the animal world, we selected only a chosen few. These are the animals we still use today, as food, or as beasts of burden.

The industrial revolution changed the way of life. Women had traditionally worked at home, earning a small income through the products of their cottage crafts. But they could not compete against the machines in mills and factories. They began to go out to work, and no longer had time to prepare meals. This soon affected the family diet in all industrialized countries, and public health authorities had to act.

In 1882, the Swiss Public Welfare Society asked Julius Maggi to find a practical solution to these problems. He was a miller, and used his skills to produce pea and bean flours. By 1884, his first powdered soups were ready for the market. These could be cooked quickly, and were nutritious. The era of ''instant'' soup mixes had begun. By 1889, Maggi had several soups. Not only in Switzerland, but also in Austria and Germany, and later in the USA. He continued to invent. First his seasoning, then the bouillon cube. He made this by lightly cooking beef, pressing it to extract the juices, filtering, skimming off fat, and finally evaporating to a thick paste. The cube retained proteins, vitamins and mineral salts of the original beef. When he died in 1912 at the age of 66, he had built up an international business with a wide variety of convenient, low cost, instant products. All of them had contributed much to public health and well-being.

BOUILLON KUB
POUR 1/2 LITRE

A L'EXTRAIT
DE VIANDE

The milky way

Milk was always our basic food. We needed it, right from our very first breath. And our mother's milk satisfied our early appetite for life.

Long before he gave up hunting and gathering, Neolithic Man in the Near East had already seen that lambs and kids were their "milk brothers". Quite naturally, we had the idea of tasting sheep and goat milk. We began to work out the best ways to exploit this life-giving white stream. Stone tablets engraved some 6000 years ago by a Sumerian peasant, record that: "between the 41st and the 49th years of King Shulgi's reign, his herd multiplied fivefold, and its yield by twenty". An Elamite seal from 2500 BC shows a peasant milking a goat. This is a homage to the goddess of fertility. Her gift of milk swelled the treasury of our foods, and set up a profitable trade. Then, in the 17th century BC, Hammurabi II introduced a tax on milk products sold in the markets of Babylon. It was inevitable that somebody would! Milk was a good thing, in more ways than one.

The early history of condensed and evaporated milk is a pure adventure story, linking fates on both sides of the Atlantic. To make it easier to understand, evaporated milk is made using heat sterilization to preserve it, and is unsweetened. Condensed milk is not sterilized. It is simply preserved by adding sugar, and so, is always sweetened.

The story started in 1856, in the USA. Gail Borden patented a process for making sweetened condensed milk, and set up a factory which supplied the Yankee Armies in the American Civil War. Soon after, at the American Embassy in Zurich, Charles A. Page became the new American Consul. He was immediately impressed with the quality of Swiss milk. With his brother George, he tried to start a business, making Borden's condensed milk from the fresh Swiss milk. Borden was not interested, so the Page Brothers founded their own Anglo-Swiss Condensed Milk Company, and began manufacture in the small town of Cham in 1866. The only thing "Anglo" about their company was that they wanted to sell their product in Britain. In the days of Victorian nationalism, they thought "Anglo-Swiss" would be better for sales. A year later, the German chemist Henri Nestlé, started up his own company only 100 miles away in Vevey, Switzerland, where he also made sweetened condensed milk for his milk food.

Henri Nestlé and the Page Brothers remained great rivals. Then, in 1905, the two companies they had founded some 30 years earlier merged into one.

We used milk to make nutritious gruels and porridges. We also turned it into cheese and churned it into butter to add savour to our best recipes.

In Pompeii, before the earthquake and the great eruption of Vesuvius destroyed the city, bakers were selling a milk-and-honey bread called picenum. In 25 AD, Apicus created "crème renversée" by mixing milk, honey and whipped eggs. One of the early specialities of the Gauls was a fat sausage called a milk "boudin" or pudding.

Animal milk has been a pillar of civilizations since Romulus, Remus and the wolf. And as we followed the milky way along the path of industrialization, it led us to the door of the modern dairy industry.

The unsweetened evaporated milk process was invented in the laboratories of the Anglo-Swiss Condensed Milk Company by Johann Meienberg. Nobody in Switzerland was interested in his discovery. So he emigrated to the USA in 1884, taking the plans for his process with him. Under the name of John B. Meyenberg, he helped start up the Helvetia Milk Company, and in 1885, the world's first evaporated milk was in the shops.

Later that year, a grocer in El Paso, Texas, bought 100 cans of Helvetia milk. His name was E.A. Stuart, known to his friends as ''E.A.''. Two years later, when the last can was opened, the milk was still perfect. E.A. ordered another 100 cans. Then in 1889, he started his own condensed milk factory in Seattle. With his partner, Tom Yerxa, he persuaded John Meyenberg to join them. Slowly, evaporated milk conquered the public, including the gold prospectors in the Klondike just across the border in Canada. E.A. found the name for his company in a tobacco shop window. A brand of cigar, called... Carnation!

Even there, the story did not end. A century after Johann Meienberg had left the Anglo-Swiss Condensed Milk Company in disgust, the Swiss-American milk wheel turned another circle. Carnation became part of Nestlé. The unsweetened evaporated milk that the Swiss had not wanted 100 years earlier, returned home to its birthplace.

Milk

and the everlasting

The food that a Tartar horseman took with him when he went on the rampage had to be light, nourishing and non-perishable.

Powdered milk is one of the "travelling foods" they invented, as far back as the 13th century. Marco Polo told us how. The Tartars boiled the milk and took away the creamy part as it rose to the top. They used this as butter. The liquid left behind contained the milk proteins and sugars. They put it out in the sun until it was almost dry, then ground it to a powder.

Every morning before leaving for the battlefields, each horseman would pour about half a pound of this powder into a leather bottle. He filled it up with water, and tied it to his saddle. During the day's riding, the movement of the horse shook the mixture, and gave liquid milk once more.

Six centuries later, powdered milk fed the troops of another army. This time, the US Army, fighting in the jungles of South East Asia during World War II. Since then, the virtues of powdered milk have peacefully conquered the world.

Up to the 19th century, milk production was just enough for the country folk, and for villages near the farms. Towns and cities grew. Cooperative dairies started up, collecting milk from the local farms and delivering it to urban doorsteps. Then, large dairy farms began to appear. By the 1930s, we were producing more milk than we needed. We had to find something to do with the excess, instead of simply letting it go sour. The answer was to dry it.

The first milk powders sold just after World War II looked and tasted like chalk. Mixing them with water gave a lumpy gruel. But at that time, milk in any form was scarce. Most of the dried milk went into bread, cakes, biscuits and sweets. Milk technologists struggled to improve the product. In 1953, David Peebles in California devised a revolutionary non-fat dry milk that dissolved instantly, and tasted very much like fresh milk. The dried milk industry had begun. Today, it produces over 5 million tons yearly. Most of this still goes into cake mixes, ice creams and desserts. But the main advantage is, it keeps for years. It can be used in hot countries to make products like cheese and yoghurt. Dried milk is now having a nutritional and economic impact in some African, Asian and South American countries where milk is not a traditional food. Here, the modern food industry is not only building milk processing factories, but is also helping local farmers create dairy farms to supply the fresh milk.

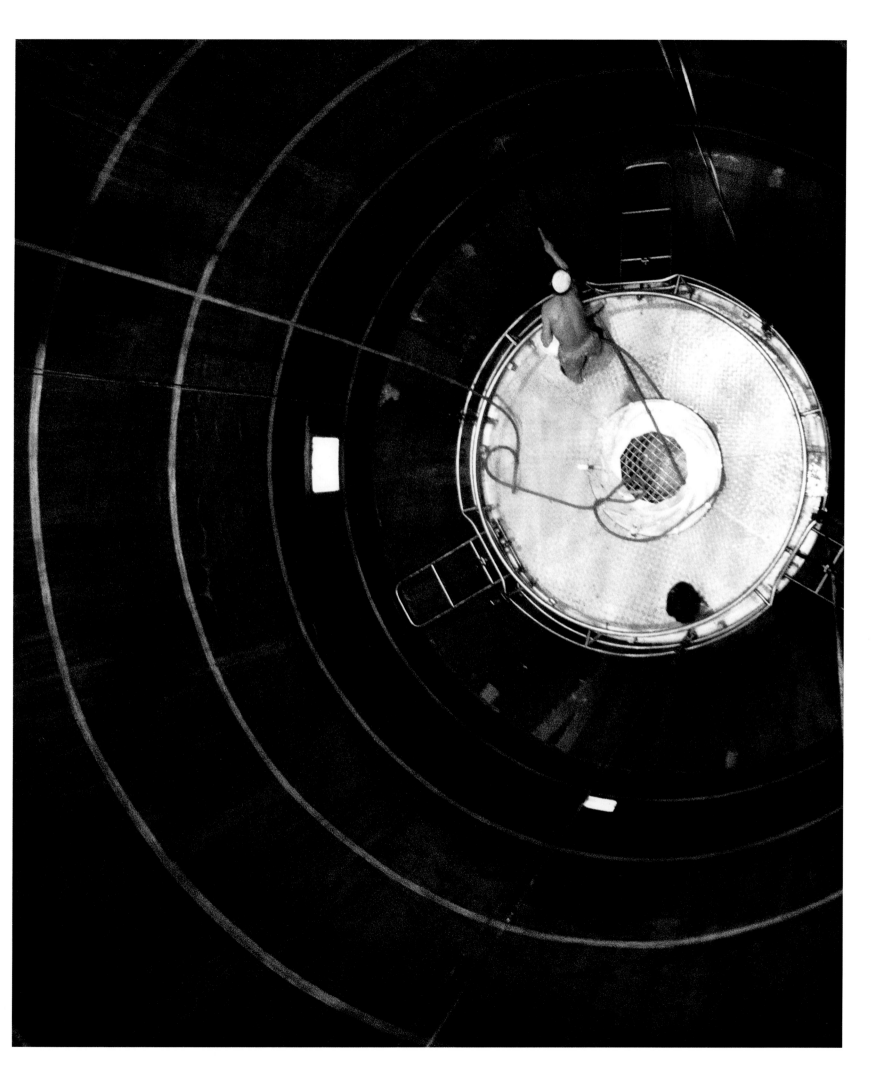

Treasures from the deep

Tens of thousands of years ago, in Paleolithic times, we were already enjoying shellfish and molluscs on the coasts and littorals. The mountains of empty shells we left behind are still visible today.

Oceans, lakes and rivers were always a rich source of food. Fish and sea mammals, as well as the animals that came to the waterholes to drink, supplied us with a wide range of meats. We also collected seaweeds and other aquatic plants. This encouraged hunters and gatherers to settle on the shores. For example, Nelson Bay in South Africa, where 400 generations of inhabitants lived on limpets, mussels and oysters they collected using scrapers made of bone.

Shellfish were so valuable that we traded and bartered them. We even used the shells as jewelry, as artistic motifs, and as money.

The first Greeks, and then the Romans, could not live without the fruits of the sea. To keep up with the growing demand, the Gauls started oyster farms. Two thousand years later, oysters are still a French tradition.

Oceans and seas cover seven tenths of the earth's surface. In them, we find over 60 000 different species of fish, shellfish and mollusc. Almost all of these are edible.

Today, we farm oysters, mussels, clams, scallops, shrimp and lobster. But also fish like tuna, salmon, trout and eel. In 1977, 100 000 tons of yellowtails were farmed in Japan. This is about 60 million fish, double the number caught by traditional fishing. Farming needs fences. In the sea, we use floating cages, set at different depths depending on the type of fish. The "farmers" often catch young, wild fish and grow them in captivity, something like the way our ancestors began farming animals over 10 000 years ago. In recent years, we have started "sea ranches" for salmon. These almost copy nature, where the wild salmon hatch in fresh waters, then head out for the open sea, and finally return to their birthplace one to four years later as mature fish. Salmon ranchers now control the early life of the fish, and hatch the eggs in rearing cages. The young "hand reared" fish are then released into the sea, but they have lost the natural migration instinct that takes them far out from shore. They usually stay within 100 miles of the rearing cage, and return "home" when they are adult. This kind of open range farming has helped to change the pink fleshed fish from a luxury food into one that is no more expensive than most other fish.

Hunters of the seas

Fishing came naturally. The site of Terra Amata near Nice contains the fossilized remains of fish we caught around 380 000 years ago, almost certainly by hand.

By the Cro-Magnon Age, techniques had improved, and we were fishing in teams. The river Vézère in the French Dordogne became a salmon reserve, where we built traps from pebbles, and caught the fish with spears. We fished in Nelson Bay, using hooks and lines made from bones and sinews, and with oysters or mussels as bait.

On the American continent, Indians made nets weighted with stones. They also built huge fish dams. One of these was found in a lagoon near Boston. It consists of 65 000 wooden piles sharpened with stone axes, and dates from 2000 BC.

The Greeks and the Chinese invented the tunny net, or more precisely, a maze of nets. Fishermen drove shoals of tuna into the maze to catch them. The Mayas and Aztecs were even more subtle. They caught enormous quantities of fish by poisoning them with pimento! Evidently not the spice of life.

Even today, the deep sea fisherman is a hunter. Like his ancestors, he needs a knowledge of the weather both above him and below him to find his prey.

Today's trawlers find shoals of fish using echo sounders. Or from planes fitted with special cameras that can see the dim light given off by fish at night. Some trawlers are linked by computer to the US Navy's navigation-satellite system. This allows them to find exactly any spot on the ocean where fish have been seen. Big commercial fisheries often send out floating factories. These process and pack the fish out at sea, so that when they reach shore, the products are ready for distributing to the shops. Shrimp, for example, are caught by trawling. On board ship, some are cooked whole in brine, to be sold as unshelled fresh shrimp. Canned shrimp are first lightly cooked to make them easier to peel, then passed through machines which remove the heads and shells. Finally, they are vacuum packed into tins or jars, which are sterilized by heating. Up to about 1960, all shrimp were peeled and packed by hand, and a typical canning line needed 200 to 250 workers. With today's automation, the job can be done by two or three workers. Machines are faster and more hygienic. They are also less costly. In fact, automatic machines have contributed much to the steady reduction in the proportion of our income we spend on food.

A fish out of water

We dried and smoked the fish we caught. They kept better, and were easier to carry back to the camp. We made thick fish pastes, and scraped off slices to use in cooking. This way, the American Indians added protein to their corn ration, and the Babylonians made fish soups.

The Cretans of Cnossos had already developed deep sea tuna fishing. Yet, the Greeks only realized the inexhaustible riches of the seas in the 5th century BC. They became virtually addicted to fish. To the point where "fish" came to mean "food in its finest form". They set up an organized fishing system, that linked the ports in their colonies around the Mediterranean seaboard.

The Romans applied their ingenuity. They kept the fish alive. They carried them in tanker ships and tank carts filled with water, or in wet sacks, seaweed and ice. The fresh fish fetched enormous prices on the markets of Rome.

Over 2000 years ago, fishing and the sale of fish were already controlled by laws and regulations. From the Middle Ages, fish became consecrated to Fridays and to Lent, and the fishing trade increased still further.

The fish stick, or fish finger, was created in the 1950s. Its simplicity hides a mountain of food technology.

Filleting machines were so complicated at first that it was faster to do the job by hand. But automatic machines now perform miracles. To start with, a conveyor belt carries whole fish from the storerooms. A machine turns the fish so that they are all lying head first, and on the same side. It then guts and cleans each fish, skins it, and slices off the boneless fillets. Flesh left between the bones is cut out by another machine, so that at the end, all that remains is the head, the tail and the backbone. By 1949, the Frukt Industri Company from Sweden, known today as Findus, was selling frozen fish fillets in Europe. Then came fish sticks. These were made by freezing fillets into large blocks, which were cut into sticks, dipped in batter and rolled in breadcrumbs. After deep frying for a few seconds to harden the batter and seal in the fish, they were cooled and packaged ready for transport.

Today, fish fingers and other frozen fish dishes have become popular. But another technological revolution lies behind their success story: deep freeze units in shops and supermarkets, and in our own kitchens. To give an idea how much frozen food we buy today, if all of the fish sticks sold in the world in 1991 were placed end to end, they would go about ten times round the equator!

Orchards and groves

Fruits were easy to pick, and we liked the taste. Fresh or dried, we carried them with us on our migrations, and transplanted them in foreign lands.

The natural gardens of Asia gave us a perpetually filled fruit basket. Peaches, apricots and citrus fruits blossomed on the bough in China, Japan and Malasia. Plums and cherries ripened in the Near East.

The wild apple was brought to the Middle East in the "picnic baskets" of invading hordes from Central Asia. It spread into Europe in time to charm Neolithic palates. It remained wild and very small until recent times, when our techniques of agriculture and plant breeding made it what it is today.

From the seeds of the first wild apple, we now have a choice of over seven thousand varieties.

Surprisingly, most fresh fruits are processed foods. They have to be processed to get them to us as fresh as when they were picked. In fact, their journey from the orchard to our fruitbowl is full of surprises. Oranges are a typical example.

First of all, the "Clockwork Orange" is real: all of the oranges on a tree are ready for picking the same day! Some might already be orange. Some might still be green. But as soon as they contain the right amount of natural sugar, they are "legally" ripe. After picking, oranges are transported to a packing factory where they pass through no less than 14 different machines. These start with a bath to cool the fruit and to kill fungus that would cause rot. On a conveyor belt, an electronic eye sorts out bad fruit. The larger fruit continue through soft brushes in a washing machine, into a drying tunnel, and through a waxing spray. They are sorted into five grades of quality and nine sizes, stamped with a trademark, and packed for shipping around the world. Green oranges may be artificially ripened with ethylene gas. Maybe the biggest surprise is that this "chemical ripening" process was invented by the Chinese mandarins... over 3000 years ago!

Today, we think it is normal to buy fresh fruit every day of the year anywhere in the world. But it is only in the past 30 years or so that we have developed the techniques and transport systems to be able to do this.

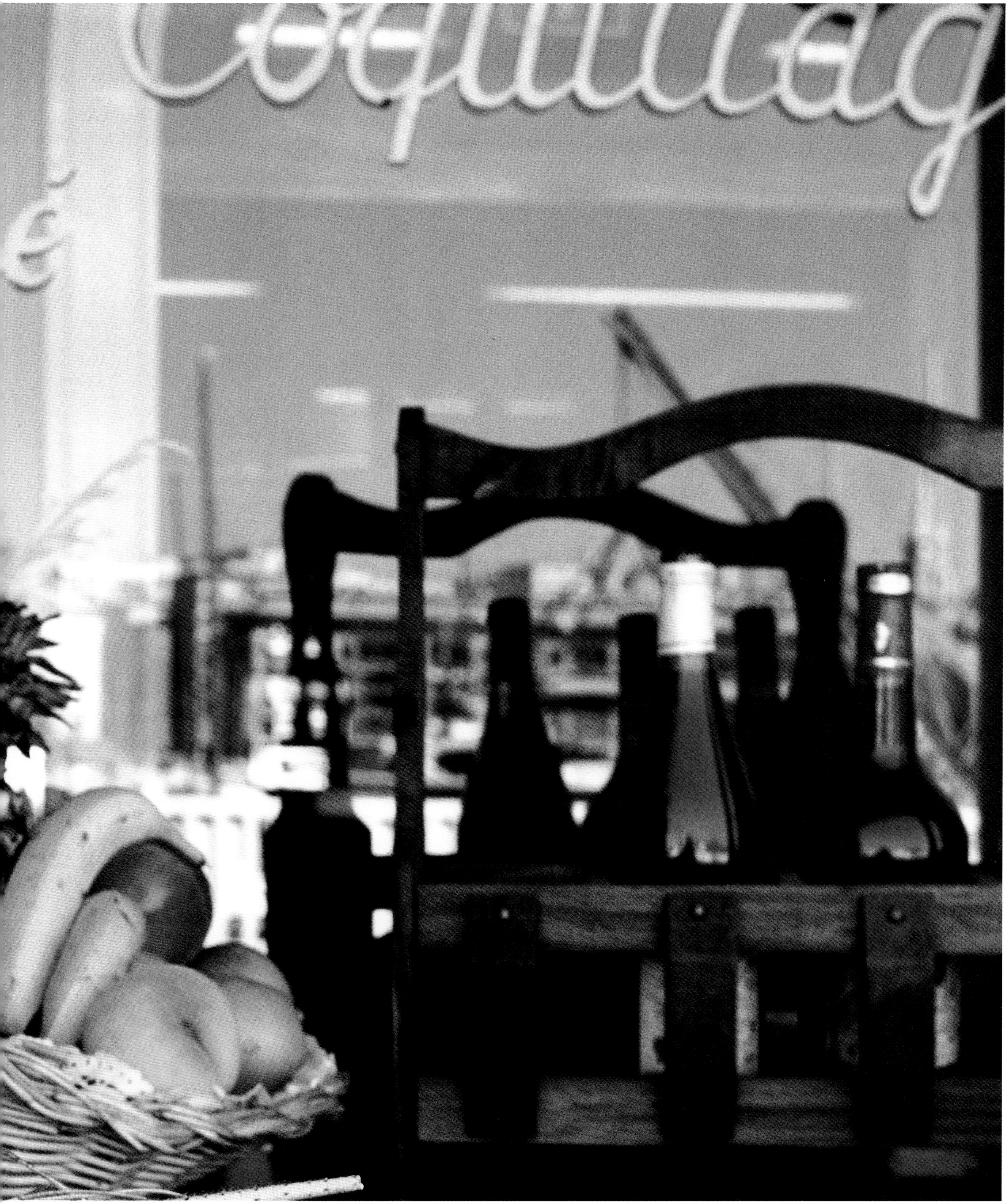

We had exploited wild apricots in the Middle East for almost 5000 years. Then we began to cultivate them. The Greek philosophers made the break-through: grafting.

This brilliant idea allowed them to "adapt" nature. They could design trees to fit the climate, and combine different varieties or even species. This way, the Etruscans, the Romans and then the Gauls, developed enormous orchards. Just as a single seed grows to give a huge tree, the single idea of grafting created the orchards and groves of the world.

Spanish explorers of the early 16th century returned from South America bringing the tomato with them. It was soon cultivated in Spain, and in Spanish provinces like Naples, Italy. Here, it was christened the pomodori, namely the golden apple or the apple that ripens with the sun, and was so popular that it became one of the basic Italian foods.

Further north, it was different. The English told fairy tales where the poison was a red apple. They believed that the tomato was the forbidden fruit of the Garden of Eden. Maybe this is also why the French call it the ''pomme d'amour'', or love apple. Slowly, it was accepted as an ornamental plant. But by the time the Northern Europeans dared to try it, the Italians and Spanish had been enjoying it for almost four centuries, and the Peruvians and Mexicans for even longer. In the USA, a land now flowing with tomato ketchup, tomatoes have only become popular since World War II. Farmers now grow some 10 million tons a year, enough for the average American to eat over one and a half pounds every week! Most of it is eaten as ketchup, juice, paste or canned tomatoes. Like the tomato, many foods which are regularly eaten in some regions are not acceptable in others. This may be for religious or cultural reasons, but is often just our ancestral mistrust of the unknown. Today's food industry takes regional and personal eating habits seriously, in offering a choice of foods from around the world.

Fruits of the earth

We turned the earth with sticks and dug with our hands to find what was hidden there: roots, tubers, rhizomes, bulbs. By tasting them, we selected the best and most nourishing, and learned to avoid those that were poisonous.

The dahlia tubers, once eaten by the South American Indians, never made it to the recipe book. But others did, like potatoes, batatas, Chinese yams, and cassava.

Leaves were certainly less filling, but they were easy to pick, and tasted fresh. Even if we did not know it, they supplied us with vitamins. Again, we selected the best, and then improved them by plant breeding. From the North African thistle, we created the artichoke. The leaves of the wild chicory, originally cultivated in Egypt, first began to curl, then gave us the endive. The cabbage grew happily in the soils of Europe. In Grece, Aristotle ate it to ward off hangovers when he was going out for a night on the town. Many root and leaf crops still garnish our tables, although fifty or more species have disappeared from the marketplace since the days of the industrial revolution.

Around the world, over one billion meals every day include potatoes! Yet, if the present food laws had existed when the potato was brought to Europe, it would have been banned.

Potatoes contain a natural poison... solanine, in green potatoes, leaves and stems. But small amounts of it are also found in the skins of normal potatoes. It gives a natural protection against insects, and is a reason why potatoes grow almost anywhere. Fortunately, this does not mean that the potatoes we buy are dangerous. We would have to eat about 50 pounds of these at every meal to have any problems! Manioc is grown widely in Africa. It contains natural cyanide, and should not be eaten fresh. Traditionally, it was soaked in water to make it safe. Then it was ground into tapioca, a food which has always had a reputation for health. Potatoes and manioc teach us one thing. They were created by Mother Nature as the ''seeds'' for other potatoes and manioc tubers, and not as food for us. In fact, none of our traditional food raw materials was ever created by nature to feed the human race! So throughout history, we have selected the safest. And now, the processing methods of the modern food industry allow us to make our food safer than it has ever been. The only danger for many of us is that we simply eat too much of it.

Market gardens

The wild bean grew in the natural gardens of Central Asia. It was eaten tens of thousands of years ago, and added carbohydrates, proteins and minerals to our diet. We domesticated it the same way as wheat.

Around 7500 BC, farmers in Thailand, Mexico and France were harvesting not only beans, but also peas, chickpeas, vetch and lentils... all brothers and sisters of the legume family. We instinctively recognized their nutritional value, and in time, they became "the poor man's meat". We had been cultivating the Mexican bean for about ten thousand years before it was introduced into European gardens 500 years ago. Christopher Columbus brought back the tomato at the same time. It slowly joined the ranks of the vegetables, although in fact, it is botanically a fruit.

The potato, grown by the Peruvians for the past 5000 years, had to wait for the French Revolution to become a regular food. But perhaps the Chinese deserve the credit for the greatest revolution in the vegetable patch... two thousand and five hundred years ago, they invented the wheelbarrow.

One hundred and fifty years ago, a factory worker would have paid a quarter of a weekly wage for a small can of beef and vegetable stew! Yet, the price was realistic. Each can was made by a tinsmith, and was so thick that it needed a hammer and chisel or an axe to open it. It was hand filled and cooked for six hours, so making a can of food took a whole working day.

Henry John Heinz was one of the pioneers of food products at prices that the working public could afford. In 1860, at the age of 16, he had already created a market garden business. Nine years later, he started a pickle and sauce company in Pittsburgh, where he was known as ''The Pickle King''. By the early 20th century, he was making far more products than his famous ''57 Varieties'', including baked beans and tomato sauce. Heinz claimed that, ''The bean is nature's most nourishing food. When baked, you eat it in its best form. It builds up body, brain and muscle''. His adverts announced, ''10 Meals for One Shilling in a Single Can''.

The main reduction in price compared to 50 years earlier had come from lower manufacturing costs. First, a good quality thin tinplate which would stand up to rough handling. Then, automatic machines to make the tins, to fill, cook and seal them, and to paste on labels. Today, automatic production allows food companies to offer even the best of luxury foods with a consistent, high quality, and at minimum cost.

The golden bean
of the land

Soya has always been a giant among plants. For its nutritional value, and for the number of ways it can be used.
The inhabitants of Northern China were cultivating it at least 3500 years ago. It has only been grown in Japan since the 7th century AD. Brought in by Buddhist missionaries, who introduced the Japanese to a new culture.

One of the greatest responsibilities of the modern food industry is to offer developing countries the agricultural and technological expertise they need to start up their own food industry. To be able to make products at prices the consumer can afford, means building factories on the spot, which employ local workers, and manufacture traditional foods from locally produced raw materials.

From a nutritional point of view, more meat in the diet would help solve the present food crisis for the 80% of the world's population still living in artisanal agricultural societies. But meat is expensive to produce, and is often forbidden for religious reasons. So the answer has to come from vegetables. Here, soya is a shining example. The soya bean contains about twice as much protein as red beans, broad beans or the pea. It is nutritionally similar to meat or milk, and along with rice or wheat, it gives a diet balanced in protein, fat and carbohydrate. Further, an acre of ground planted with soya produces enough protein every year for 15 people, where the same acre would only produce enough beef for two people. It is not surprising that the ''Golden Bean of the Land'', as the Ancient Chinese called soya, has become today ''The Gold Nugget of Nutrition''.

We prepared and cooked soya in a multitude of ways. Sometimes, to make many different dishes in the same meal. We ate it fresh, dry, germinated, fermented, or ground into flour. We made it into pastas, gruels, sauces, soups, drinks, oils, cheeses and desserts. And we even used it to pay taxes to fill the treasuries of the Japanese Emperors. Up to the 20th century, Western civilizations ignored the gastronomic and nutritional value of soya. They used it simply as a fodder for fattening animals.

Then, they struck liquid gold. The yellow oil they pressed from the soya bean was recognized as a valuable food ingredient.

Soya is not the perfect food. No food is. But it is an ideal staple crop. In the homes of South East Asia, it is still converted into many products, including the traditional soya milk. This is prepared by grinding beans in water, filtering and boiling, and has about the same protein value as cows milk. In the home, it takes all day to prepare, and it must be drunk the same day. Today, it can be made industrially.

Curded soya bean gives tofu. Roasted beans are ground into flour, but more nutritious flours come from soya mixed with wheat or corn. There are many fermented products, like the well-known soya sauce that flavours Chinese food. Also fermented whole beans, tempeh and natto, as well as miso, which is made from soya and rice. Soya oil is good for making margarine, and the solid cake left after pressing out the oil contains so much protein that it can be used in place of meat.

The soya bean processing industry started in 1908 in Hull, England, where they extracted oil from Manchurian soya to make soap! Most of the modern soya industry is now centred in North America. South East Asia grows only 15% of the world soya crop, but this increases every year, with more soya plantations, and with factories to manufacture the traditional soya foods. Using soya as a base, some parts of Asia, Africa and South America are now treading the path leading to the modern food industry.

Spice fever

The Romans liked good food. They spiced it to widen their spectrum of delicate flavours. Before that, we had used spices more as air fresheners or purificators than in foods. They were part of religious ceremonies. We used them in life as in death, as cosmetics and perfumes, as medicines, and as part of the embalming ritual for Egyptian mummies.

Spice traders carried their wares on camel trains and in ships, from the Indies, to Egypt, Syria and Lebanon. From there, they sent them all around the Mediterranean.

The Renaissance thirst for discovery pushed explorers to look for what lay beyond the waters of the Mediterranean. The Spanish, the Portuguese, the Genoese and the Dutch set sail to the East, attracted by the scent of treasure.

In spice boxes and pomodors, the heady aromas of distant lands conquered the kitchens of Europe.

Spicery was recognized as a trade about 800 years ago, when the Pepperers' Guild was created in London. By the time Richard the Lionheart came to the throne, English spicers were already selling pepper, nutmeg, cloves and ginger. The spice shop became the grocer's. In France today, a grocery store is an ''épicerie'', coming from ''épice'', meaning spice.

Pepper, from India's Malabar Coast, was the first spice imported into Europe during the days of glory of Ancient Rome. We now use over 100 000 tons of black, white and green pepper every year. Black pepper is picked when the berries are ripe and red. The outer skin turns black as they dry in the sun. White pepper is also picked red, but is soaked to remove the skin, leaving the white seed underneath. Green pepper is picked before the berries ripen and is sold without drying. The first spice ships were often attacked by pirates on the infamous Barbary Coast. Pepper was worth more than its weight of silks, noble metals or precious stones: aristocratic societies were ready to pay a fortune for food that tasted good.

We now take ''pleasure in eating'' for granted, and here, the culinary value of spices is still a good foundation. The modern spicery sells not only dozens of spices and herbs from around the world, but also, subtle mixtures, expertly blended to make our foods fit for a King at prices that fit the average purse.

The roasted bean

According to legend, the coffee plant came from Kaffa in Ethiopia. But it was first used in the Yemen, by an imam. Watching a herd of goats, he saw how they became excitable and active after browsing on the red berries. He tried them himself, drinking a brew he made by boiling roasted and crushed beans in hot water and honey. The miracle happened. The Imam stayed awake all night, his mind as clear as a bell.

In the 9th century, the Persians drank a coffee called qahwa. From that time on, it spread through all Islamic countries. Prosper Alpino became the first European to drink qahwa, in 1580. Then in 1650, the Turkish Ambassador Soliman Aga persuaded Louis XIV to taste it.

Coffee drinking in the 17th century had its problems. The berries cost a king's ransom, and they had to be dried, peeled, roasted and ground by hand before they could be brewed. But the coffee trade was under way. Oriental coffee houses soon decked the vibrant streets of 18th century Europe. They offered the perfect surroundings for sampling the exciting black liquid, and for meetings that would transform the world.

It is said that the first coffee tree in Brazil came from French Guiana, where the punishment for taking plants out of the country was death. A young Brazilian army officer was sent to French Guiana with strict orders to bring back a coffee plant. He courted the favours of the Governor's wife. When he returned to Brazil, she gave him a cutting from a coffee tree which he smuggled out in a bunch of flowers. Coffee won a reputation for romance, and Brazil won a battle.

Instant coffees date back almost a century. The first products were coffee crystals, liquid coffee concentrates, and a mixture of coffee and milk known as the coffee cube. However, they neither tasted nor smelled like coffee, and very often did not dissolve. In 1930, Brazil produced so much coffee that some of it was even burnt. Brazilian officials contacted the Nestlé company, who were already manufacturing milk products in Brazil. Their idea was to use the mountain of beans to make coffee cubes. But there was a snag. Brazilian law only allowed the manufacture of pure coffee products, and the coffee cube contained milk! The problem was transferred to Nestlé's research laboratories in Switzerland, where Hans Morgenthaler made a powdered coffee in 1937. Two years later, just in time for World War II, one of today's best known convenience products went into industrial production.

Turning over a new leaf

Before we began to drink tea in China, we made it into cakes of pressed leaves... and ate it! Civilization progressed. By the 6th century, tea had become a popular drink associated with the exalted spiritual values of Taoism. The Chinese also invented fine porcelain, sold later as chinaware. The decorative teapots and cups made tea drinking an art.

The taste for tea spread to Japan in the 11th century. Tea drinking became a ritual, precisely orchestrated to achieve a purity of spirit and an aesthetic perfection.

Tea arrived in Europe in the 17th century. In Britain, it became an institution. By 1834, British planters had started to grow it in Northern India and in Ceylon, and began to rival the Chinese on the world tea market.

"Orange Pekoe" from Ceylon, "Assam" and "Darjeeling" from India, the Chinese "Pekoe, Lapsang, Souchong, Yunnan", and "Earl Grey". Smoked, perfumed, expertly blended, the names paint pictures of the venerable and harmonious gardens where generations of tea pickers have braved the midday sun.

Almost everything about tea is traditional, even to the methods used in today's tea manufacturing industry.

The fresh young leaves are still picked by hand. They are dried in hot air for a day, then rolled to crush the plant cells. This releases natural enzymes that ferment the leaf, forming the tannins which turn it from green to brown. After firing to stop the fermentation, this gives us black tea. For green tea, fresh leaves are steamed in a blanching bed. This kills the enzymes, so there is no fermentation and no change of colour. Oolong tea is half fermented, and is neither black nor green, but somewhere between the two. Most of the teas we buy are blends, mixed from different pure teas. This makes sure that we always get the same flavour in our cup from one year to the next. Jasmine flowers, mandarin orange peel, bergamot and other sweet herbs can also be blended in.

This century, there has been one major break from tradition. The tea bag. It was created by a tea merchant in 1905 as a high class convenience product: a silk bag, tied at the neck with a string. His customers were intended to open the bag and empty the weighed quantity of tea into their teapot, then fill up with water as usual. But it did not take long to see that the whole bag could be put in boiling water. And the teabag had been invented. We now find this Cinderella of the tea industry, dressed in paper instead of her silken gown, in every supermarket.

Indian bitters

The story of cocoa begins with the Maya gods, who drank a brew made from something called Cacahuaquchtl, which they found in the virgin forests of Yucatan. Much later, a medical thesis dated March 20, 1685 described cocoa as "the only true food of the gods".

The Aztecs in turn became lovers of chacahoua. They used the beans as money. They offered them to Cortez in 1523. The conquistador accepted the gift, and carried his treasure back to Spain. From there, chocolate took the courts of Europe by storm.

Up to the 17th century, chocolate was so heavily taxed that only the very rich could afford it.

Inventors devised the techniques of evaporation and moulding, and in 1770, the first chocolate factory was built in France. Chocolate found a second home in the 19th century: in Switzerland, where Daniel Peter created the first milk chocolate in his Vevey factory in 1875.

Chocolate is a fine art of flavours, colours and textures to charm the gourmet palate. Raw cocoa beans taste bitter. Our ancestors made them more appealing by fermenting and roasting them to develop the cocoa flavour. We still use the same process in the modern chocolate factory, along with an astonishing amount of technology.

Roasted beans are first crushed, and ground to a thick paste. When hard, this gives bitter cooking chocolate. Cocoa powder comes from working the paste with bicarbonate to make it less bitter and acid, then pressing out the cocoa butter, and grinding the solid residue into a powder. For fine, eating chocolate, the paste is mixed with sugar or with sweetened condensed milk, and forced through a series of rollers to grind the granules down to a smooth, velvety liquid. Cocoa butter is then added, and the ''conching'' process begins. The original ''conch'' was a large, shallow seashell where, in ancient times, the chocolate paste was stirred slowly by hand with a wooden paddle. Today we use a machine, which is fortunate, since conching takes three or four days. Exactly why conching works is still a mystery, but it develops the full chocolate flavour. The brown liquid is then poured into moulds, cooled, and finally ''tempered'', to give a fine chocolate, which is solid at room temperature, soft to bite, and melts in the mouth.

In the press

We probably made the first fruit juice by crushing wild berries with a stone or a log.

By 6000 BC, we were certainly pressing juices through sieves or colanders. Remains of these primitive tools have been found in excavations on the shores of Lake Neuchatel in Switzerland. We then had to wait till the 3rd century BC, when Archimedes invented the screw. One hundred years later, the screw press had been developed, and a refreshing river of grape juice oozed from the vineyards of Athens.

From fruit juice to wine was only a single step. All we had to discover was the secret of controlled fermentation.

Wine is so traditional in continental Europe that any serious attempt to replace it by pasteurized grape juice would surely cause another French Revolution. Yet, this is exactly what happened to the hard bitten pioneers of America's Wild West.

Up to the mid 19th century, hard cider was the national drink of the Americans. At the time, it was impossible to prevent the fresh apple juice from fermenting. Social pressure from temperance societies encouraged the food industry to find ways of manufacturing unfermented apple juice. However, this was not really a substitute for hard drinks like cider, beer and whisky. So we saw the birth of a major new industry. Soft drinks! In the complex jungle of the law, pure fruit juices do not qualify as soft drinks, because legally, a soft drink is a mixture of ingredients. It may include fruit juice, and often has, since the fountain of soft drinks began to flow a century ago. The number of flavours which can be created by mixing different fruits, herbs and spices, is infinite. So from a simple idea of mixing fruit juice, or fruit essence, with sugar and citric acid, in still or fizzy water, we now find a bewildering variety of squashes, crushes, cordials, pops and colas. New flavours of soft drinks are born every year. A few become traditions, and for these, the recipes are guarded like the gold of Fort Knox.

Golden sugar

Cane sugar was a luxury. We looked on it as a medicine "worth its weight in gold". Then, sugar became an industry, and thousands of poor wretches were reduced to slavery to work the plantations.

The Ganges delta in India seems to be the source of the sugarcane. Like wheat, it was a wild grass. As long ago as 12 000 BC, we gathered this to make "honey without bees".

Conquest upon conquest, invasion upon invasion, we spread the sugarcane far and wide all through the Middle East and to the Mediterranean islands. About five hundred years ago, soon after the famous voyage of Columbus, the cane was transported to the New World. In the West Indies, it flourished with the exuberance of youth, and the abundant crop fed the refineries of Europe.

The golden brown, sticky crystals slowly replaced honey in satisfying the sweet tooth of the human race.

We have used refining since Antiquity to extract the edible parts of plants in the form of food ingredients. These are more convenient to use than the whole plant, and easier to preserve or store. On Sugarcane Road from India to the Caribbean, sugar refining has always been part of sugarcane cultivation. The reason is evident: the raw cane rots in a few days, but the extracted sugar or syrup keeps for years.

Modern refining is carried out in two stages. First, on the plantation, the cane is mashed and pressed, then treated with calcium salts to give a clear juice. On evaporation, sugar crystals form in the thick liquid. Spinning in a centrifuge gives crystals of dark brown, raw sugar, and liquid molasses. The liquid is sold in several grades, from the light brown molasses which contains the most sugar, to black treacle which contains the least. There is also a grade called Blackstrap which contains almost no sugar: this is added to the residues of the sugarcane after pressing, and goes to feed cattle. The raw crystal sugar is then sent to a central refinery where the second purification is carried out. Partly purifying gives demerara sugar. Complete purification with bone charcoal to remove the last impurities gives white sugar. Between the two, several shades of brown sugar may also be produced. This second purification stage also gives a molasses, but of a higher grade, usually sold as golden syrup, or confectioner's syrup.

Sugar from the soil

Cane sugar stood unrivalled in our sugar bowls. Until the 16th century, when Olivier de Serres "discovered" a new sweetness, in sugar beet. This root crop grew abundantly in the soils of Europe.

The discovery lay buried until the 18th century, when a German chemist called Marggraf showed that the sugar from beet was exactly the same substance as cane sugar. In 1802, François Achard, a French chemist found an easy way to extract sugar from beet on a large scale, and started a small factory. But nobody was particularly interested. The traditional cane sugar was still much less expensive than beet sugar, and it tasted better.

New processing improved the taste. The price came down to affordable levels, and beet sugar broke the sugar cane monopoly.

The real breakthrough for beet sugar came with the Napoleonic Wars. The English blockaded French food supplies, including cane sugar. In 1810, Benjamin Delessert who was Director of the Bank of France, financed a beet sugar refinery near Paris based on Achard's process. In 1812, Napoleon ordered the planting of 300 square kilometers of sugar beet to provide raw material for the factory.

There was only one problem. The French public did not like the new product. It was identical to cane sugar, except for a slight taste of beet, but the public thought that it was less sweet and generally inferior. By the time the English blockade ended, Napoleon had made Delessert a Baron for his services to France. But the product was still unpopular, and as soon as cane sugar was available again, beet sugar production was stopped. About a century ago, production started again, using better beet and better machinery. This time, the public was convinced. Beet sugar became a common product, to the point where we no longer ask whether we are putting ''beet'' or ''cane'' in our coffee.

This story shows two faces of the human race. First, our ingenuity in making new food products. Second, our suspicion of the new foods we create. Innovation and Suspicion. These keys for survival accompany us through life, and prove that we have not lost the natural instincts of our primitive ancestors.

The holy unction

The olive tree played a prominent role in biblical, Egyptian and Greek legends. It was a symbol of glory, peace, purity and prosperity, and yielded up its noble spirit in the form of olive oil.

We were pressing oil 5000 years ago on the Eastern Mediterranean shores. It was the birthright of the Phoenicians, the Cretans and the Egyptians. They became great traders in the golden green liquid, which they used for food, for perfumes and medicines, and for religious rites.

At first, we trampled the whole, ripe olives underfoot in a huge earthenware mortar. Then we crushed them to a pulp with a pestle in big, hollowed out stones, and strained out the precious oil through straw matting.

Sicily, North Africa, Spain, France. One after the other, the olive invaded their lands. It spread to the Americas at the time of the Renaissance, and then to Australia and South Africa. Yet, it has kept to its traditions. Even in the 20th century, cultivation and processing of the olive are still mainly carried out by the methods of the artisan.

Olive oil is one of the aristocrats of food. It anointed the heads of olympic champions in Ancient Greece and Kings in Europe. From 5000 years ago, it has stayed almost unchallenged for its fine flavour and nutritional qualities. The ''olea'', namely the olive tree, even gives us the word, ''oil''.

Rapeseed oil has no such airs of grandeur. It comes from the ''rapa'', a sort of turnip. Its other name is colza, from the German ''Kohlsaat'', meaning cabbage seed. In fact, botanically, the rapa is part of the lowly cabbage family. The cabbage was always a food for the poor: so when we started in the 17th century to extract cabbage seed oil, its social level was automatic... in the kitchens of peasant cottages. We used the oil for cooking right up to this century, when experts began to think that it might be harmful to health. The ''danger'' came from erucic acid. This is in all oils, but at the high levels in rapeseed oil, it was thought to be bad for the heart. Plant breeders from Canada came to the rescue. They created new varieties of rapeseed with almost no erucic acid. Today, Canada alone grows over 4 million tons a year, and in the world, rapeseed oil accounts for 12% of all edible vegetable oils produced. Experts now recognize its nutritional value once more. So the ''oil of the poor'' no longer needs to hide behind the name of ''salad oil''. It can take its rightful place beside olive oil, as the humble cabbage becomes a king.

Edible oils

The climate in many parts of the world was not suited to growing olives. But many other plants grew, from which we could extract oil by pressing the germ, nuts, seeds or pips.

In Brazil, we took the native peanuts, crushed them to a pulp. We then boiled them with water so that the oil separated out. It floated to the surface, where we skimmed it off, and used it for cooking. The Sioux Indians in North America made oil from sunflower seeds. This oil combined lightness with a subtle nutty taste. Sesame oil was much appreciated in India and around the Mediterranean.

Corn, rapeseed, ricebran, sesame, soya, safflower, sunflower, almond, coconut, hazelnut, peanut, palmnut, and walnut. Cottonseed, grapeseed, hempseed, watermelon seed. Argan, cameline, karite, poppy and rocket. Each of these, in its own way, swelled the streams of oil used in kitchens around the world.

As they mature, the seeds of any plant begin to store oils. These are the ''baby foods'' for the young seedlings of the next generation. Corn, cotton, olive, peanut, rapeseed, soya, safflower and sunflower seeds give us most of the edible vegetable oils we can buy today. They are all made using basically the same method and machinery.

Seeds are first crushed with a mechanical press to squeeze out the crude oil. Small particles of seeds are removed by filtering, or in a centrifuge, or by simple sedimentation. The oil is then washed with water to take out gums and resins, and treated with bicarbonate to neutralize any acidity. Most crude vegetable oils are highly coloured, so they are ''bleached'' by filtering through bone charcoal. The oil is deodorised by bubbling steam through it. Finally, it is ''winterized'', by cooling in a refrigerator so that tiny crystals of solid fat separate out. This prevents the bottled oil from going cloudy in the kitchen cupboard, even during the coldest days of the year.

Today, in our research for new edible oils, we have tested almost two hundred different nuts and seeds. These include all of the common vegetables, fruits and spices, and even seaweeds and mosses. One or two, like blackcurrant seed oil and kiwi seed oil, have an especially interesting nutrient balance, and will certainly find their way into the foods of tomorrow.

Buttered on both sides

When we began breeding livestock in the Middle East, this opened the way to dairy farming. From then on, we saw cows, goats, gazelles and sheep in a different light. As farms became more organized, we developed the techniques of milk production and processing.

The Sumerians kept their best yielding cows in corrals, separated from the rest of the herd, and churned the milk into butter. This was about six thousand years ago. Butter was common in Egypt, but the Greeks and Romans looked down their noses at it. They were faithful to the majestic olive, and butter was the poor cousin.

Butter in the Middle East was made from sheep or goat's milk. The Tibetans used yak's milk. Cow's milk butter was prized by the Celts and the Vikings, and spread through Western Europe, following the Norman conquests in the 11th century.

Cooking with butter, or cooking with oil? A spaghetti curtain still divides culinary habits from the north to the south of Europe.

Cream is an emulsion of tiny particles of milk fat in water. Churning gives butter, which is also an emulsion, but made of droplets of water in milk fat. This natural blend of water and fat gives butter its texture and spreadability.

The traditional butter making process meant waiting a day till the cream floated to the top of the milk, then ladling it off for churning. In 1877, Gustav de Laval, in Sweden, invented the centrifugal cream separator. He fed a constant stream of fresh milk on to a rapidly revolving disc, and spun the cream off. This brought the dairy industry into the mechanical era, and a typical factory now turns over 100 tons of cream per day into butter. Yet, butter has kept its 19th century traditions. The buttercup yellow colour is still obtained by adding carotene, the natural pigment of carrots. The first margarine was invented as a butter substitute in France by Hippolyte Mege-Mouriès in 1869. It was an emulsion of water in beef fat.

Modern margarines are made from hydrogenated vegetable fats. With the right fat, and the right amount of water, we can reproduce exactly the texture of butter. Or even improve on it, as in margarines that spread straight from the fridge. Margarine has often been seen as unnatural and synthetic: an inferior substitute for butter. But is this really so? Like butter and olive oil, should we not see them both as food products in their own right, each offering us a choice that suits our personal eating habits.

The world's smallest workers

We had been fermenting our foods for thousands of years before we found out how fermentation worked. But this was not important. It did work, and that was good enough for us.

Fermentation happened naturally. We watched how nature did it, and then we tried it ourselves. After many failures and disappointments, we managed to recreate the right conditions. Many times, our fermentations would go wrong, and then we would have to throw the whole brew away and start again.

As with many of our early discoveries, our pragmatic methods served us well. Starting from Neolithic times, our fermented cereals, milk, honey and fruits, were among our very first processed foods.

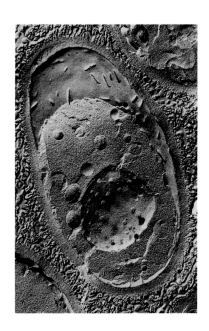

Fermentation can make food more nutritious, more digestible and safer, and can improve the flavour. But more than this, it is a powerful preserving method which mainly uses natural biological energy. Many fermented foods keep with little or no refrigeration. So fermentation is one of the best and cheapest methods to preserve food in hot, humid climates.

Living micro-organisms are the key to fermentation. For most living species, life starts off as one tiny cell, which multiplies to billions of cells during growth. But micro-organisms spend their whole life as a single cell, so small that 50 000 of them would fit on the head of a pin. These include yeasts, bacteria, moulds and viruses. We now know that the world is full of micro-organisms. Some are valuable for processing our foods. Some cause food poisoning and disease. Throughout history, we have had to sort out which was which. Our ancestors did this empirically. If it made them ill, they did not eat it again. Then, almost 3000 years ago, they started domesticating the useful ones, exactly as they had done with plants and animals. Long before we knew how to control it, fermentation took its place along with cooking as a method of food processing.

Following on from our ancestors, we have learned, during the past 100 years, how to specifically direct the fermentation of different foods. And another traditional food process which is as old as the hills could finally be used in industry on a large scale.

Fresh
from the baker's

The development of agriculture and cereal farming brought new riches into the household.

We can imagine one day, that an ancestral housewife left a batch of cereal dough aside. Airborne spores of yeast seeded it, and it began to ferment and swell. She baked it anyway, not wanting to waste the precious food. And the bread which rose up from her Neolithic baking bowl filled the air with its yeasty aroma.

Since then, we have made bread from barley, buckwheat, corn, oats, rye, spelt and wheat. These seven cereals were the foundation stones of the baking industry.

Over 4000 years ago, the Egyptians began to master bread making. They kneaded their dough in bowls, and put it in preheated baking moulds which they stacked in a sort of conical kiln. The Assyrians baked their barley or wheat bread in hot earthenware dishes. When the Greeks invented the first modern oven, baking became an art and a trade.

Yeast is the secret of bread. It gives the typical spongy structure by forming small bubbles of carbon dioxide gas from carbohydrates in the dough. The first yeasts were the ''barm'' that was skimmed off the top of beer we were brewing. Bakers began to cultivate yeasts by keeping a part of the dough they had just made to mix into the new dough the following day. Up to 50 years ago, our bread yeast was essentially the same as that used in the bakeries of ancient Egypt.

In the 19th century, ''yeast factories'' started up, and yeast ceased to be a by-product of brewing. The factories produced barm cake, which was a mixture of yeasts, and distributed it fresh to bakers every day. In the 1930s, the more active strains were purified out to give ''thoroughbreds''. These raise the freshly made bread dough more quickly. So compared to his ancestors, today's baker saves time, and makes bread of the same quality every day. The new yeasts can also be dried without losing their activity. We have even discovered that yeasts catch viruses, and how to cure them when they are sick!

Today, factories for the breeding, raising and health care of yeasts have now become a part of the food industry, supplying all of the fresh yeasts for industrial baking, and the dried yeasts used in the home. These new developments add to the trade secrets passed on from master bakers to their apprentices, right from the first bakers in history.

Everyman's ale

German brewers wrote the most recent chapter in the story of beer. But the first brewers were the Sumerians and the Egyptians.

A sort of ale is described in some of the world's oldest writings, dating from Babylon around 4000 BC. They brewed it by soaking barley or wheat in water, letting it germinate in the sun, then boiling it, and fermenting the infusion. This was then thickened with flour to make a nourishing "drink". Fortifying and slightly inebriating. It could be drunk as it was. Or it could be baked in the ashes to give a sort of raised bread.

Brewing was a well established art. But it had developed empirically. Jacob Christian Jacobsen believed strongly that science was the means to make it even better.

In 1835, at the age of 24, he inherited a brewery in Copenhagen from his father, who was a self-taught brewer. He visited several breweries in Germany, and learned how to brew lager beer. This had to be brewed cold, and his success came when he was granted a royal license to use the cool cellars buried under the thick walls of the city. In 1847, he founded a larger brewery, built on a small hill — or ''berg'' — just outside Copenhagen. He named his new brewery ''Carl's Berg'', after his 5-year old son Carl, who was destined to be his successor. In his first year, he produced 350 000 litres of lager, about the volume brewed every two hours today.

Liquid bread or solid beer? Whichever they were, fermented gruels weaved their way from one country to another. They even took hold in Greece, then Gaul, Spain and the Adriatic coast.

The Roman Emperor Domitian was partly responsible for this. To protect his Italian vineyards from foreign competition, he enacted laws that prohibited wine growing in Gaul. The resourceful Gauls changed over to growing cereals. They invented the barrel, and soon rolled it out, full of barley beer, or ale. This became the popular drink of Northern Europe. It was cheaper than wine, and Celtic, Welsh and Irish warriors quaffed it by the gallon.

Flemish and German monks in the Middle Ages began to add hops. In the cloistered halls, the thick, brown ale, became a clearer drink with a characteristic flavour: beer.

The modern manufacturing process for beer involves 16 steps. Specially grown barley is steeped in water, then germinated to give green malt. After drying in kilns to develop colour and flavour, the malt is crushed, mixed with water and heated to 76°C. This gives a liquid wort, where the cereal starches have become malt sugar. The wort is filtered, boiled in huge coppers with hops, then sieved into fermenting tanks and cooled to 12°C. Yeast is added, and the wort fermented for 7 to 14 days depending on the type of beer. The brew is then matured for two to four weeks in aluminium tanks which hold about 10 million litres. After centrifuging to remove any yeast that remains, the clear, sparkling beer is filled under pressure into bottles, which are automatically crowned, pasteurized, labelled and crated. All at a rate of 78 000 bottles per hour from each production line!

J.C. Jacobsen would not have believed these astronomical production figures. Although he himself created the means to achieve them, when in 1875, he set up the first research laboratory in a food company. He believed that through it, his son Carl could become ''Europe's leading brewer''. In the laboratory, top level scientists worked on each step of the brewing process. So successfully, that they not only established his company as a leading name in science, but also cultivated the *Saccharomyces Carlsbergenis* yeast, used today by all breweries around the world making lager beer.

A thousand cheeses and a 100 year-old yoghurt

The Sumerians wrote down the first recipes for making cheese: a white cheese they made from goat or sheep milk. They left the milk to curdle in skin pouches, then simply put the curd in reed baskets or on braided matting to drain.

The Greeks used this in pastries or rolled it in balls and stored it in brine. The Romans ate it smoked or spiced. The curdled milk slowly became real cheese, as we invented special moulds to preserve and mature it.

The Huns and the Mongols discovered the secret of fermentation. Not just to make cheese, but also to create yoghurt, with its distinctive flavour and smooth texture. Yoghurt, the Balkan secret of longevity, only reached Western Europe after World War II.

There are 78 different blue cheeses and 36 Camemberts among the thousands of cheeses made around the world. Blue cheese needs two bacteria for the fermentation: a *Streptococcus lactis* to help curdle the milk, and a *Penicillium* which gives the blue veins and forms a natural antibiotic that helps preserve the cheese. Camembert also starts off with a *Streptococcus*, but the curd is then sprayed with a mould to give the white, soft interior, and to create flavour.

More surprisingly, salami is also a fermented food. It is made by adding *Pedicoccus* or *Lactobacillus* to chopped raw meat, with salts and spices. This is fermented 3 days at 90% humidity and 30°C, then dried in a stream of air. Drying takes 12 weeks, and is done in special rooms where humidity and temperature slowly drop to 65% and 15°C. Traditionally, salami was made in wooden huts, warmed by the sun and built on hillsides to catch the breeze. Humidity, temperature and aeration were regulated by opening and closing flaps in the walls. This was only possible when the climate... the wind, temperature and humidity... were just right. For modern fermented products, we simply create the right climate artificially, all year round. Today, fermentation is reaching the heights of perfection.

Scientists have now worked out how to make all the holes in a cheese the same size! Only one country could have made this discovery! Switzerland, land of precision.

Inebriating nectars

Mythical honey fed both god and sage with its sweet and mellow purity. Ordinary mortals yearned to share in this golden treasure made, they thought, of sunlight.

The wild bees vigorously defended their nectar. We called on our reserves of cunning and courage to ward off their stinging attacks. The way we gathered our honey is recorded in a 12 000 year old fresco on the walls of a cave in Spain. This shows a honey collector hanging from a cliff face, holding a basket, and surrounded by a threatening cloud of bees, as he extracts the honey with his hands from a hole in the rock.

The Egyptians battled the swarms with spears, exchanging sting for sting. Then, they captured and domesticated the bee, using hollow trees as the first beehives.

We ate honey raw, as a sweet seasoning. We also turned it into mead, by mixing it with water and fermenting it in the sun. Drinking this oldest and simplest of alcoholic beverages, both god and man could get drunk as lords.

Few foods have a purer and more natural image than honey. Yet, the beehive is a real biotechnological food processing installation. A hive of industry in every sense of the term.

Bees visit about two million flowers to get enough nectar for one pound of honey. The sweet, watery nectar contains sucrose, better known as common white sugar. In the beehive, the bees deposit the nectar in the honeycomb. They turn it into honey by evaporating the nectar till it has a sugar content of 80% or higher. The higher it is, the more crystalline the honey. But first, they add two enzymes. One breaks down the sucrose to give a mixture of glucose and fructose, called invert sugar. This mixture gives the bees an instant energy food for their intense activity. Diluted with nectar, it becomes the ideal baby food for young bees. The second enzyme is a food preservative. It keeps out harmful bacteria, and also discourages yeasts, which would ferment the nectar into alcohol, unusable by the bees. Apart from honey, there is also a second production line in the hive, to manufacture the Royal Jelly the bees feed to the Queen.

Making either honey or Royal Jelly, the beehive is a real food factory, with sugar refining, enzyme hydrolysis, preserving agents and biotechnology. Strange that when bees process their foods, we call it ''natural'', but when we humans do it, we call it ''industrial''.

The vines of the Lord

The wild vine had grown, apparently since the dawn of time, in the Miocene in Western Europe. The glass bottle came later. We invented it in the 1st century AD. In between, we had worked with the gods to turn the pressed juice of the grape into wine. A drink, that could reduce gods to human proportions, and give men fleeting illusions of being on a higher plane. We were making wine over 6000 years ago in the Middle East. Cultivation of the vine arrived in Egypt, where we developed the noble arts of viticulture. This led to the wine trade, and to legislations written in the hands of Mesopotamian scribes. Wine traders spread their wares to the East, through Persia and India. And to the West, along the trade routes for amber and tin.

The Greeks dedicated their great grape harvests of over 5000 years ago, to Dionysos, god of wine. The convivial drink became the source of the symposion: the original after dinner speeches where Plato and fellow philosophers spoke of love and constructed the world. From 534 BC, wine also inspired Athenian playwrights, and gave wings to the actors' tongues.

In 1695, Dom Pierre Pérignon became cellar master at the Abbey of Hautvilliers in Champagne. His work on wines lay at the crossroads between art and science.

His main discovery was blending green and black grapes to get the same high quality of wine every year. We cannot know for sure if he created champagne itself, but the ''champenoise'' method of making sparkling wines became a tradition. The bubbles come from adding grape sugar to still wine, and fermenting a second time in the bottle. Different amounts of grape sugar give Brut, Extra Dry, Dry, Semi Dry, or Sweet Champagnes. Bottles are stacked neck down so that the yeast collects behind the cork. Freezing the neck gives a solid plug, which is blown out, or ''disgorged'', by opening the bottle. This is then refilled with wine, recorked and wired ready for sale. We now have easier and cheaper methods to make sparkling wines: doing the second fermentation in large tanks, then filling the bottles under pressure; or carbonating the wine directly with gas, like a fizzy soft drink. These new methods give the bubbles, but they lack champagne's ''fizzical'' appeal.

Then, we have the different glasses used to serve champagne: the cup, the flute, and the tulip. These may have a star cut in the glass to ''seed'' bubbles, and make the wine sparkle even brighter. In fact, the art and science of the tableware used to serve food and wine is just as much a part of the food industry as the food itself.

Al'koh'l vapours

Distillation is an ancient art. We used it in the Near East and around the Mediterranean to distill out the living spirit, and capture it as the "water of life". From the 4th century BC, Aristotle refers to using an alambic for turning sea water into fresh water.

Paradoxically, the first written details on making pure alcohol came from an Islamic country. A Persian sage, in the 8th century AD, wrote down the secrets of distilling wine.

The crusaders were so charmed by the spirit of the still that they took the alambic back to Europe. With the blessing of Saint Patrick, the Irish began to drink the juice of the barley. The first official whisky distillery was established in 1276, in Ireland. No doubt to the eternal chagrin of the Scots, who would have liked to have been the first to receive the spirit.

If fruit juices are simply allowed to ferment naturally, the alcohol level reaches a maximum of 15%. The brew must then be distilled to get to levels of 35% or higher, typical of spirits and liqueurs.

The ancient art of the still was propelled into the modern food industry in 1830, when Aeneas Coffey invented his new distilling unit. In Coffey's still, the brew was filtered down through a stack of plates with small holes. A current of steam was forced up the stack, and carried off the alcohol in a continuous stream. Today's stills work on the same principle. Distilling fermented brews from grain, fruit or roots, gives spirits with no colour. The typical colour of whisky or brandy comes from storing the spirit in oak barrels which have previously contained sherry, or from caramel. The name, brandy, comes from ''brandewijn'', which is Dutch for ''burnt wine''. So the word ''brandy'' just means ''distilled'', and applies to any spirit. However, food laws in most countries define brandy precisely, as distilled grape wine. Thus, Cognac and Armagnac from France, Metaxas from Greece, Grappa from Italy, and Pisco from Peru are all brandies, while the brandy distilled from cherry wine is called Kirsch, and cherry brandy is a liqueur.

Only the spirit of the law could make things so simple!

We fermented all of the different cereals, and distilled out their spirits to lift up our own.

Italian Jesuits made liqueurs from grapes and other fruits. They used these as medicines. The pleasant tasting brews became so popular that they began to trade in them.

In the rough life of the early American colonies, Anglo-Saxon settlers distilled a mixture of corn and malted wheat, and obtained bourbon.

Liqueurs are flavoured spirits. They are made by soaking fruits, herbs, spices or flowers in the pure spirit, then redistilling or filtering. Coffee, chocolate or cream may be added, and they may be sweetened with sugar syrup.

Benedictine is one of the famous liquours. It was created in 1510 by the monks as an elixir of life, and is flavoured with 27 herbs and peels. But this is nothing compared to Chartreuse, commercially manufactured, even today, by the Carthusian monks, using 136 herbs and spices!

Again, the long arm of the law steps in. Chartreuse is banned in the USA, because the labelling laws require a listing of all ingredients. Here, there are two problems. First, the monks do not want to give away the secret formula of life they have kept since 1607. And second, the label on the bottle is simply not big enough!

Multiplying microbes

We learned to use the produce of nature with ever increasing skill. But nature was capricious. Most of our fresh foods rotted or decomposed if we did not eat them immediately.

We tried many methods to preserve them. Among our frequent disappointments, a few of our efforts worked. We did not know why, but we did not need to know. We could now begin store our foods, and this improved our chances of surviving the lean seasons. Our empirical preservation methods helped develop the food trade. They gave us the means to carry perishable foodstuffs from the rural regions where they were produced, to markets in the growing towns.

Drying, smoking, freezing, heating. Pickling in acid, salt, fat, honey, sugar or alcohol. Using these traditional methods, we made our foods immortal.

Microbes are everywhere. In the earth, the air, in water, on our hands and clothing. They are so tiny that we can only see them with a microscope. Some help to make our food tasty and digestible. Others cause sickness and food poisoning.

Hygiene to combat the "bad" microbes is imperative wherever food is handled. This includes the home kitchen. Microbes find enough food to survive in tiny knife cuts on wooden cutting boards, in cracked dishes, in corners where grease and dust build up, in damp dishcloths. This is why the design of kitchens and utensils is an all important part of the food industry. Eating a single microbe, even one that might cause food poisoning, is not really dangerous. The natural defences in the body kill it before it can do any harm. The problem with microbes in food is that they can double every 20 minutes. From only one microbe, we have 2 after 20 minutes, 8 after 1 hour, and so on, until we reach 64 billion after 12 hours! Keeping foods from going bad means preventing this multiplication from happening.

In the 19th century, Pasteur made his great discovery: that food putrefaction and food poisoning were caused by microbes. From then on, the food industry has developed preservation methods that work surprisingly well... considering the millions of microbes around us all the time.

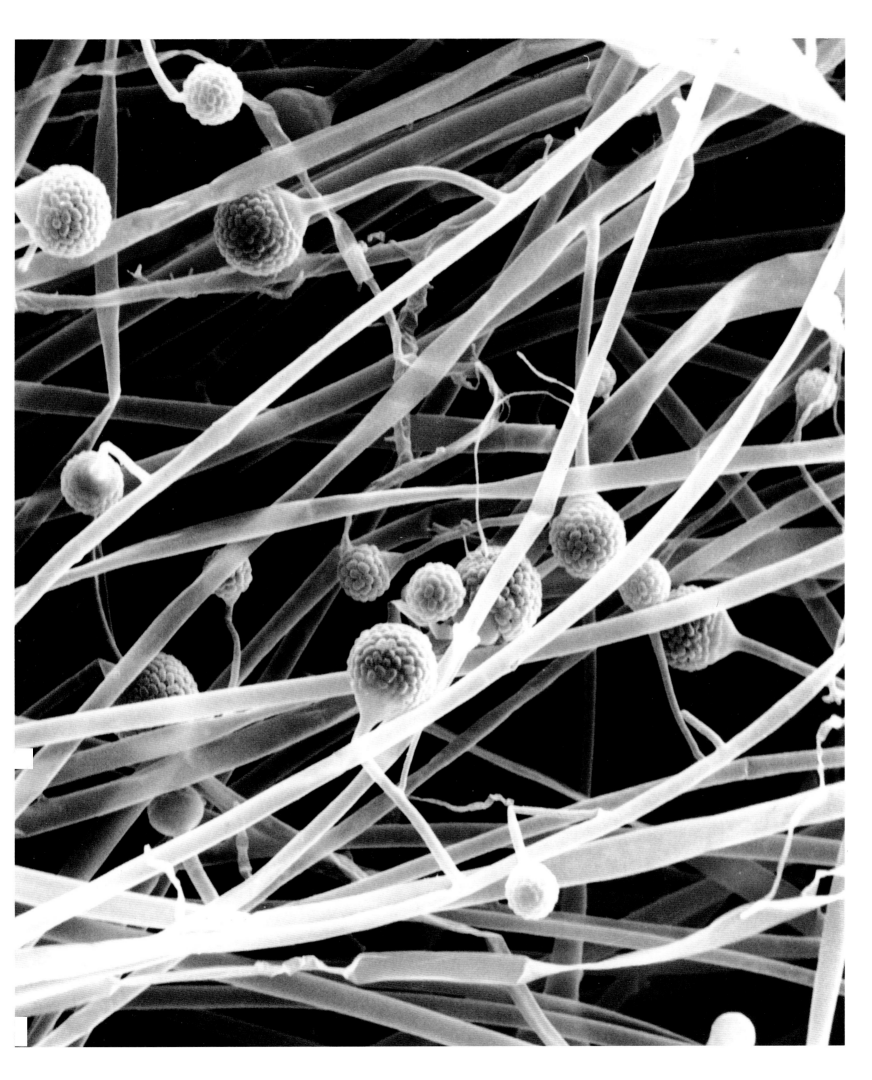

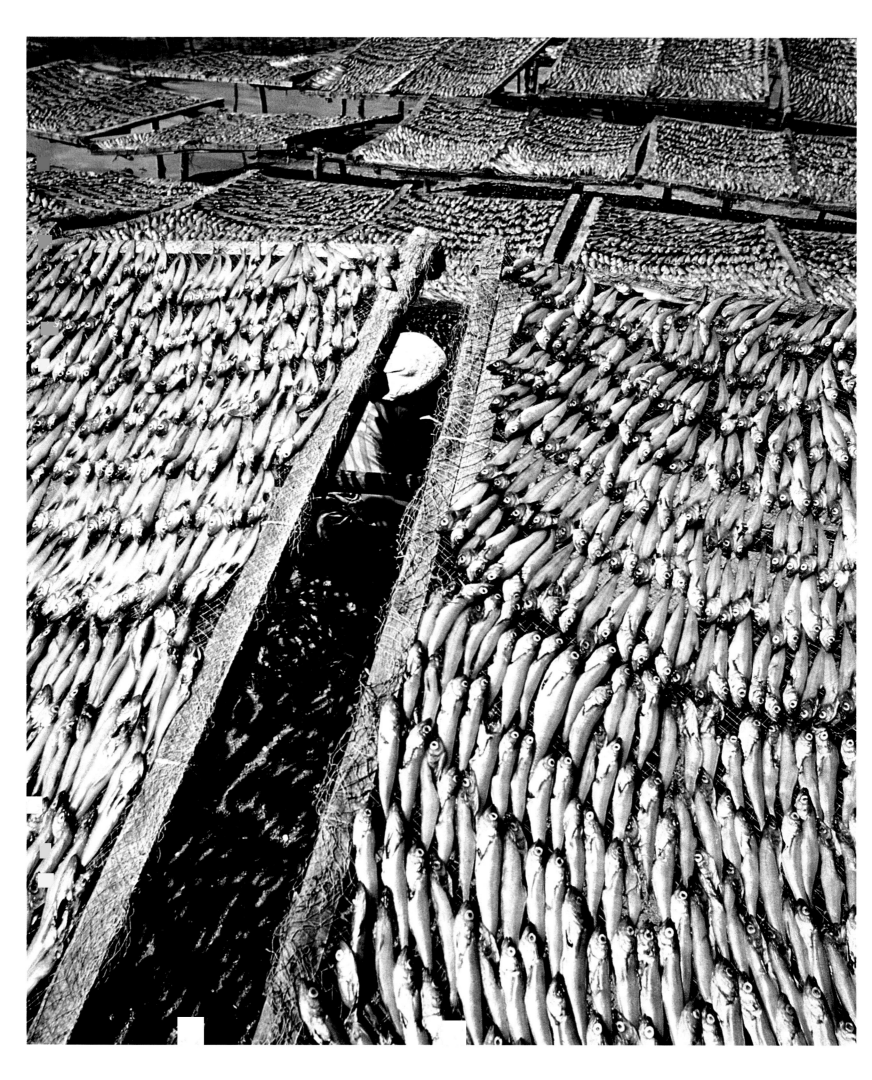

Drying and smoking

The heat of the sun and the pure, dry air. These were the first processing aids we used to preserve our foods.

The South Americans made tasajos by cutting their meat into strips, coating these with cornflour, drying them in the sun, then winding them into little balls. The North American Indians, the Celts and the nomadic tribes of Asia Minor ground sun-dried meat into a powder. They mixed this meat flour with water, and drank it. The Vikings used the wind and the sun of the Great North to dry one of the most perishable of all foods: fish. We also dried fruits and vegetables... like a bean from the Andes which was grown over 8000 years ago, and is still preserved today.

We needed no technology to dry our foods. Just the right climatic conditions. Smoking foods was different. Here, we had to wait till we could control fire. Once we had done this, we used smoking widely. Right from Mesolithic times, we smoked fish in the south of France.

For thousands of years, drying and smoking were all we needed to preserve almost anything we ate.

Microbes need water to live. Any fresh food contains enough water to keep millions of them multiplying happily. So drying is still widely used today in food preservation.

Freeze drying, or lyophilization, is one of the most impressive of the new preservation methods. It comes from a traditional process, used in South America since the days of the ancient Incas, to make chuño, a sort of instant mashed potato. They could only make this in winter. They froze slices of fresh potatoes on the mountain tops in the cold night air. During the day, the ice crystals in the potatoes sublimed under the winter sun like white frost from rooftops, leaving dehydrated potato pieces.

Modern freeze drying dates back to 1906, and to Arsène d'Arsonval and F. Bordas in France. By 1955, shrimp and crab were dried by this new process. One of today's most common freeze dried foods is instant coffee. The factories are huge refrigerators about the size of three tennis courts, four or five floors high, and cooled down to $-20\,°C$. This creates an artificial mountain-top climate. Machine operators dress for the Arctic conditions, in fur-lined boots, parkas and gloves. After freezing the coffee extract on a conveyor belt, ice is removed in a vacuum. The solid ''coffee cake'' is ground to give granules, and these are sealed in watertight jars or packets, to provide a product as fresh as percolated coffee.

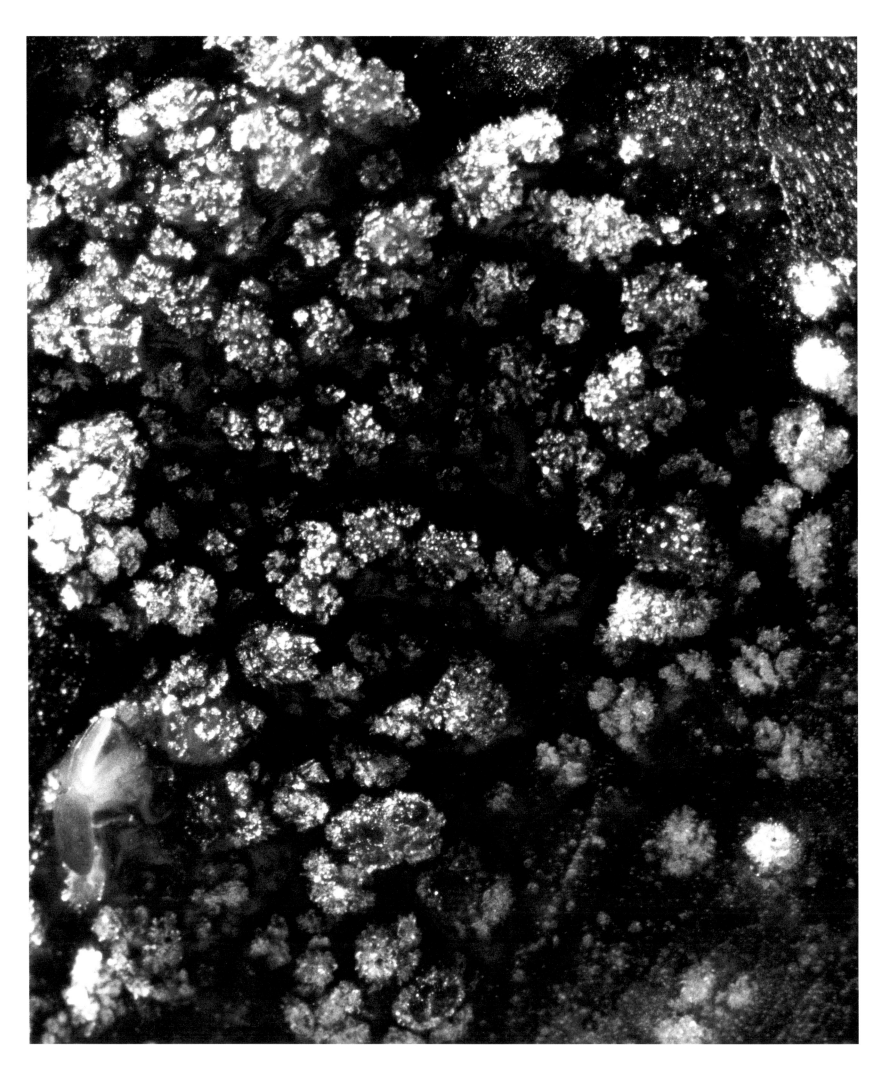

In the icebox

It was simple. All we needed to do to preserve our food was to find a cold place to store it. In Paleolithic times, we used the back of the cave. More recently, this became the cellar.

In the mountains and near the Arctic circle, freezing our foods was evident. In fact, much of the time, it was unavoidable. Vikings and Scandinavians preserved game and fish on ice. The inhabitants of Newfoundland buried codfish in the snow. The Eskimos on Baffin Island refined the technique. They salted their food before they froze it, to get a double preserving effect.

From Antiquity, we transported fish to inland towns preserved in ice. The Romans built cold storage warehouses, and supplied refrigerated foods as luxury items. And according to rumour, the Emperor Nero invented sherbert ice by mixing crushed fruit juices and honey with snow.

Bringing nature into the kitchen. This is exactly what Clarence Birdseye did when he started preserving foods by deep freezing. And so successfully that frozen food portions have become a major sector of the food industry.

Birdseye got his idea by observing nature. In 1916, he worked as a fur trapper in Labrador, where the Eskimos often left food outside to freeze in the sub-zero temperatures. This kept food fresh for the winter months. Returning to the USA, Birdseye began to experiment. By 1924, he was producing 500 tons of frozen fruits and vegetables per year. These often tasted even fresher than fresh foods because they were frozen as soon as they were picked. He found that the texture was better preserved with faster freezing, which gave smaller ice crystals in the food. So he invented a freezer that froze the product from both sides at the same time. In 1935, he created the multiple plate freezer, used by the whole frozen food industry today to manufacture a wide range of products.

But the commercial success of frozen foods depended on completing the cold chain by making fridges and freezers for shops and for the home kitchen. The first ice machines had been seen as an offence to God, because ''if he had wanted us to have ice all year round, he would have arranged the world that way''. In spite of this, the home refrigerator was built by 1913, and a fridge with a small, separate freezer compartment appeared in 1939.

Heat sterilized

We cooked our food. We noticed that it kept longer than if we left it raw. Maybe not so much with cereals, but certainly with meat and fish.

We noticed it, and we used it, without question. Right up to the 17th century, when scientists began to ask why heat preserved food. Francesco Redi was a naturalist and a poet. He studied the worms that infested rotting meat. He found out that these hatched from eggs laid by flies. This went against the established ideas of religious scholars, who thought that all creatures, including worms, arose from a divine act of spontaneous generation. The Jesuits were even more dismayed when Leeuwenhoek discovered microbes under the microscope he had built. After this, men of religion damned the tiny, malevolent microbes as the work of the devil.

The English priest, John Needham, and the Italian Lazzaro, were the first to see that foods could be sterilized. Yet it was a French confectioner, who showed the way... Nicolas Appert, who preserved meat, milk, peas and beans by boiling them for hours in clean, tightly corked glass bottles.

When Nicolas Appert opened a factory to make canned food, the whole food industry took a huge step forward. Up to then, much fresh food had gone bad. But when supplies were short, we had even eaten the bad food. The result was food poisoning. In the early 19th century, over 80% of deaths came from infectious diseases, often passed on in food.

Appert began experimenting in 1795. Many disappointments later, he succeeded. In 1804, he persuaded the French navy to test his fruits, vegetables and meats. Scientists tried to explain why Appert's method worked. The famous Joseph Louis Gay-Lussac pontificated that ''oxygen caused putrefaction, and that the food was preserved by driving out air''. This was totally wrong. But Gay-Lussac's scientific reputation was so great that his error is recorded even today in almost every cookery book, and may contribute to many accidents with home preserves.

Louis Pasteur gave the correct explanation in 1861. Namely, heating food kills microbes, and sealing it in jars or cans keeps other microbes out. Removing air was just coincidental! As well as explaining Appert's success, Pasteur's work led to a new method. Pasteurisation. This involved lower temperatures than Appert's sterilization, and the foods tasted better. The new method was soon in use for preserving acidic foods like fruits and pickles. Because of their natural acidity, these do not need total sterilization.

Progress was rapid. Tin cans replaced the glass bottles in England and Holland. By 1815, London canners were sterilizing fruit by steaming. The first factory for canning sardines in oil opened in 1824, in Nantes, France. And the USA entered the industrial era of canned food. Appert had started one of the biggest sectors of the emerging food industry. But he died poor, without ever seeing his nephew's invention of the autoclave in 1851. Then two years later, the American Winlow "perfected" sterilization. Or so he thought!

While French scientists argued about why Appert's canning process worked, British technologists and businessmen went into action.

In 1810, Peter Durand took out a patent, using tin cans instead of glass bottles, to ''preserve perishable foods a long time from perishing or becoming useless''. The idea was taken further by Donkin, Hall and Gamble, who became leaders in the canning industry, until they were bought out by Edmund Crosse and Thomas Blackwell. The early canners advertised their products by sending them to the Royal Family, to the aristocracy and to the Admiralty, with a ''humble request'' to write a recommendation which they could publish in the newspapers. This way, many of them earned the right to print on their labels, ''By Appointment to the Royal Household''. At the 1851 Great Exhibition of London, the public saw mountains of canned food on display, including instant whole dinners!

Then came the scandal. The British Navy wanted cheaper canned foods. Their manufacturer cut costs by cutting corners, and his products went bad in the tins. The whole food industry got a bad name, and it took half a century to come out of the cloud. Finally, in the 1890s, Samuel Cate Prescott and William Lyman Underwood translated Pasteur's scientific explanation of canning into the modern, controlled technology we have today.

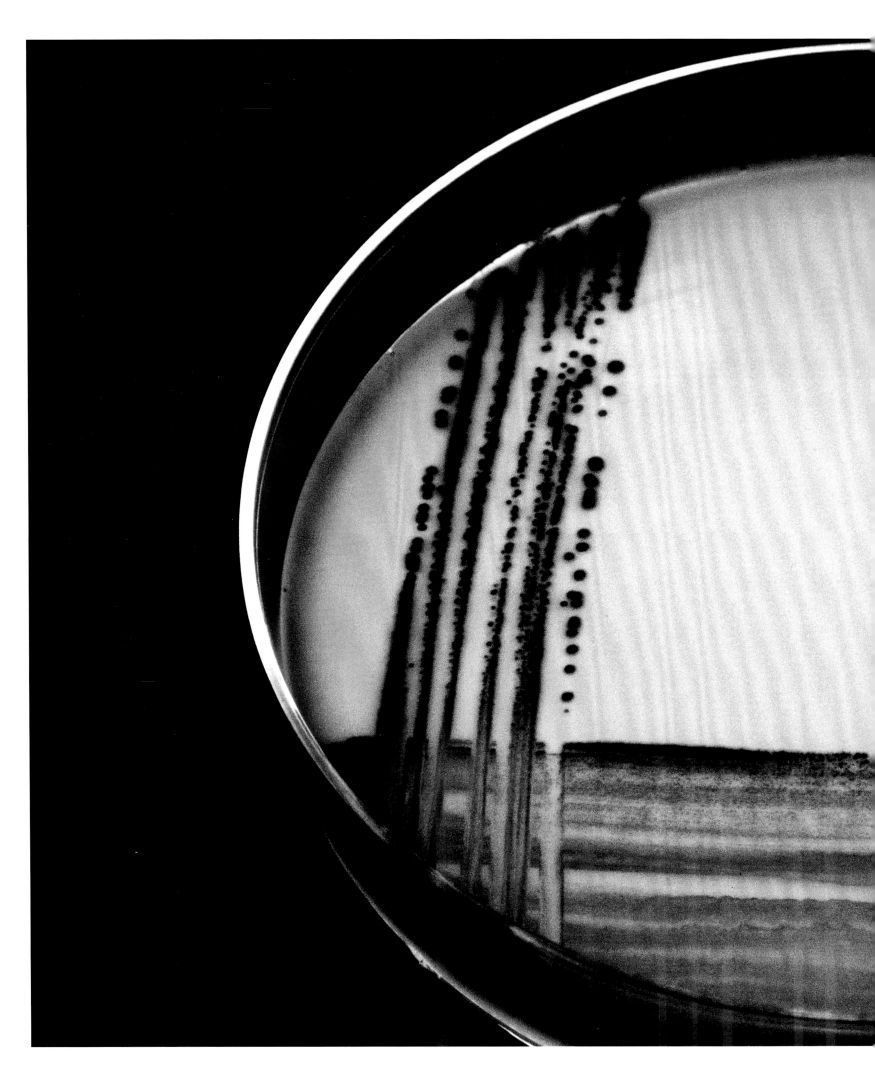

A certain acidity

One of our foods in Neolithic times in Northern Europe was an acid soup. We made this from young birch twigs, buds and leaves, which we fermented and salted.

Up to the 16th century in Europe, we used the same methods to preserve herbs, nettles and thistles. The Germanic tribes also made their own contribution to the European menu. They shredded cabbage, then fermented, salted and spiced it, to give sauerkraut. They ate this easily digestible food raw or cooked. It became so popular in Central Europe that it was one of the first foods we produced industrially.

Sauerkraut was surprisingly one of the keys to success in Captain Cook's voyages of exploration. Although he did not know it, sauerkraut contained calcium and iron, along with vitamins A, B1, B2, C and niacin: micronutrients which kept his crew fit and healthy.

The most common acid we use in and on our foods is vinegar. It is a dilute solution of acetic acid with a sour taste, and its name literally means sour wine. It was used in Ancient Rome to sterilize drinking water, and today, it is the basic preserving ingredient in pickles.

Most fruits contain acids: tartaric acid in grapes, malic acid in apples, oxalic acid in rhubarb, and both citric acid and ascorbic acid in lemons, limes and oranges. These acids protect the fresh fruit against microbes with a sweet tooth. They also make it easy to preserve fruits by pasteurization. Foods like milk are not naturally acidic, but can also be preserved by acidification. A typical example is yoghurt. The milk is often ''scalded'' first to kill any undesirable microbes. Then, live microbes called *Lactobacillus bulgaricus* and *Streptococcus thermophilus* are deliberately added! In spite of their unappetizing names, these preserve the milk by fermenting part of the milk sugar into lactic acid. But they do not know when to stop, so we finally have to kill or deactivate them so that the yoghurt does not become too acid. This means pasteurizing them, or keeping them in the fridge at temperatures where the microbes will grow only slowly.

Vinegar, natural acids, or acids produced by fermentation. All are frequently used in the industrial preservation of many common foods.

Cured in salt

We needed salt to live. We took it from the beds of dried out lakes, from underground deposits, from the seashore. We carried it along some of our first trade routes to parts of our growing world where it was not naturally present.

Around 500 BC, the Celts worked huge salt mines in the Austrian Alps. They set up an international salt business. The Phoenicians also based a rich commerce on the "white gold". And what had been a simple overnight staging post on the salt road grew into a civilization of conquerors: Rome!

We made brine by mixing salt with water, sometimes with herbs, spices, saltpetre and potassium sulphate. Brine had a culinary career of its own. We used it as an alternative to salting to preserve fish. The Egyptians had a more curious tradition. They used brine to pickle a highly nutritious seed, the lupin.

Strangely, none of our civilizations thought of dedicating salt to a god. It stayed in the hands of civil authorities, who used their power to impose heavy taxes on it.

Salt may be the most important condiment we have ever used. The sodium it contains helps regulate the mechanism of the heart. Our ancestors were blissfully unaware of this, but they knew instinctively that without salt they would die.

Before the days of canning, meats and fish were "cured" with salt. We rubbed salt into the surface of the food, then hung it in canvas bags or packed it in barrels. This preserved it by drying. Bacon is one of the oldest cured foods, already common in ancient Rome. Up to the 20th century, it was looked on as a food for the poor and for sailors. In fact, by modern standards of juicy, lean bacon, the original product was tough, hard and rancid. But at least, it was not attacked by microbes. Meat technologists now have new processes for curing bacon. They start with pork belly, sides and back, and mechanically tenderize the meat by micro-cutting the muscle fibre in a machine with hundreds of tiny knives. It is then marinated in brine, containing vitamin C, sugar, citric acid or lemon juice, gelatine and wine. The new method holds the water in the product, so it does not keep as long as the old salt-dried bacon. But this usually does not matter, since few of us today have to store it for six months without a refrigerator. Thanks to modern technology, a tough, old product with an inferior image, is now tender and juicy, and a real pleasure to eat.

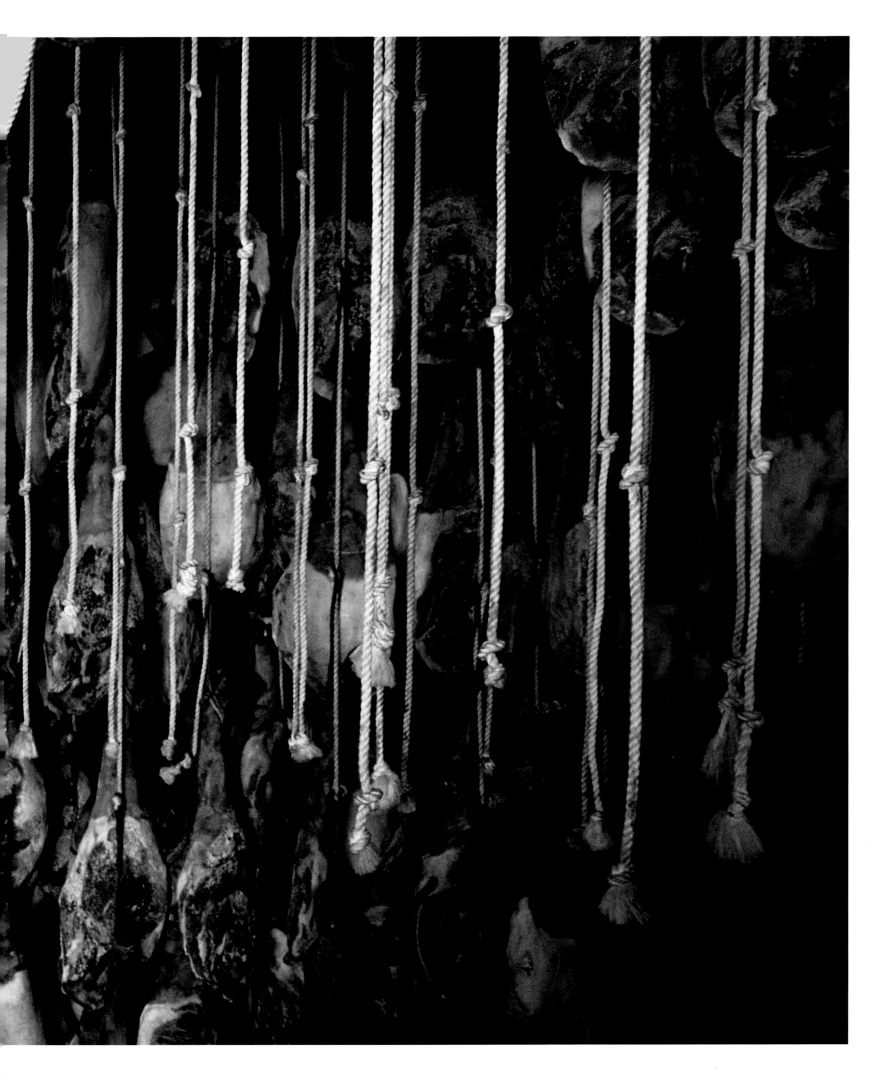

A protective layer of fat

We clothed ourselves in animal skins. We used their bones and antlers as tools. We ate their meat. Then we discovered that covering our foods in animal fats preserved them. The versatile and timeless olive oil also served once more, to preserve cheese, vegetables and fish.

The Gauls reached new gastronomic heights with their goose and pork conserves. The early Eskimos used the whale. They could not hunt it. But nature was bounteous, and whales were sometimes stranded on the shores. Four thousand years ago in Thulé, the "whale civilization" lived on the giant mammals. In the Middle Ages, whale bacon was a basic food for hard times. And more recently, we used whale oil in margarines.

Cod liver oil also became a standby. To preserve... health.

Traditional Dutch gouda cheeses are preserved with a layer of red wax on the surface. This acts like a sort of flexible ''can'' that keeps out microbes, water and air. In fact, fats and oils are often used combined with other preservation methods like drying, fermenting or sterilization.

Pemmican is one of the oldest foods preserved in fat. The North American Indians made it by grinding dried meat, adding wild berries and fruits, mixing it with fat, and packing the mixture like a sausage in a piece of animal gut. It could be stored for months. But it also showed their sense of what we now call a ''balanced diet''. The meat gave them protein, the fat energy, and the berries vitamins. Early in the 19th century, before canning and freezer ships existed, fresh meat was transported to Europe from Australia packed in barrels of fat. The Frenchman La Pérouse, who gave his name to this method, may have seen it used in his native country to preserve goose flesh in jars.

Today, oil is used more often than fat: for packing sardines, pilchards, tuna, salmon. We still use waxes for sealing foods like wine, liqueurs and mustard in bottles closed with corks. The wax, usually red, also gives an eye-catching image of quality. But whether fats, waxes or oils are involved, the basic principle for today's food manufacturer has not changed. To keep the goodness in, and the dirt out!

A sugar coating

China, India, the Middle East, Egypt, Greece, Rome... In fact, almost everywhere in the world, we learned to use the golden protection of honey to preserve fruits, flowers, seeds, stalks and even meat.

Around the end of the Middle Ages, we began to make crystallized sweets. We dipped dried fruits, juniper berries, or spices like cloves, ginger and aniseed in melted sugar. These satisfied our sweet tooth, and we even took them as medicines to settle the digestion. The idea of sweets probably came down from the Greeks and Romans, and their custom of handing out sticky bonbons called "tragmeta" to celebrate weddings and births.

Nostradamus wrote a treatise on marmalades, stewed fruits, fruit pastries and jams served at medieval feasts. During the Renaissance, confectioners surprised the world with novel ideas: rose jam, a marmalade of violets, lettuce in syrup, crystallized celery, and many other sweet delights.

When sugar prices dropped to levels the average mortal could afford, a new preservation industry emerged. Confectionary.

If we can get a whole orange grove from a single orange seed and a good farmer, what can we get from a boatload of oranges and a grandmother? For James Keiller in Dundee, Scotland, the answer was simple. In 1797, he got a food company.

His maternal grandmother had taught his mother how to make ''marmelat'', a quince jelly. Then, his father, John Keiller bought a whole cargo of Seville oranges from the captain of a storm battered ship that arrived at the Dundee docks from Spain. The oranges were so bitter that even the hardy Scots would not eat them. But John Keiller had a keen nose for business. His wife got out her mother's recipe for marmelat, and cooked them, along with sugar from John's grocery shop, in her home kitchen. She thus created the bitter-sweet Dundee orange marmalade. This even contributed to public health, because the vitamin C from the oranges helped to fight scurvy. Marmalade quickly became so popular that Mrs. Keiller founded a company with her son James. Climbing on the train of the industrial revolution, James and his brother Wetherspoon, mechanized production to make marmalades industrially.

This romantic story from the mists of Scotland hides one of the principles of the food industry. We will only eat foods if they taste good. The Keiller secret was to turn the nutritious, but inedible Seville oranges into something we liked to eat.

Pickled in alcohol

From ancient times, fruits, vegetables, meat and fish have sought refuge in the preserving spirit of alcohol.

Alcohol itself is virtually imperishable. More than this, it kills microbes, so it keeps food from going bad. The Greeks preserved fruits in grape brandy, and the Byzantines pickled pears in wine. We tenderized meat by marinating it in alcohol or wine. The wine added new flavours and aromas. It also added tannins that came from the grape skins. These reinforced the protective effect of the alcohol through their own antimicrobial powers, and delayed decomposition.

Finally, we added wines and spirits to our recipes for cakes and sauces. This lifted our daily fare from the ranks of mediocrity to the heights of gastronomic delight.

It is easy to imagine how chocolates with hard centres are made. Simply pouring melted chocolate over a solid piece of nougat or caramel, and letting it set. But covering a liquid centre to make chocolate liqueurs is a different story.

The ''griotte'' is a cherry, used to make a Swiss speciality, ''chocolate covered griotte-in-kirsch''. In the factory, cherries are stoned at a rate of 300 every minute in a sort of ''sewing machine'' with a thick needle. The outer chocolate shells are small cups made by pouring melted chocolate into moulds. These are turned over before the chocolate hardens, so that only a thin layer sticks to the surface. Another machine drops a stoned ''griotte'' into each cup, then fills this up with kirsch liqueur. A thin layer of liquid chocolate is spread over each cup to close it. After solidifying in a cooling tunnel, the mould is turned over one last time to release the chocolate with the liquid centre.

The whole manufacturing method depends on a few simple principles of nature: in the product, the alcohol sterilizes the ''griotte'', while the chocolate coating keeps the liquid in and keeps microbes and air out; in the process, all operations are based on heat, cold, and the law of gravity. This kind of simple combination of biology and technology is typical of the food industry in any age.

The fat of the land!

Wild geese migrated every year. Before taking wing, they always gorged themselves with food. This gave them the energy they needed for the long distances they had to fly.

The Egyptians were the first to observe this. Or at least, the first to exploit it. About 2500 BC, they domesticated the goose. They ate the fatty goose liver as a delicacy. Then they had the idea of force feeding their flocks, so that the domesticated geese developed the same fatty liver as their wild relations. A tomb from the 5th dynasty, in the Louvre Museum in Paris, illustrates the force feeding process, engraved in the cold and timeless stone.

The Greeks fattened geese and ducks, with wheat crushed in water. The Romans used dried figs. And Apicus, the famous gastronome of Rome, fed his geese on honey to improve the taste even further.

Our ancestors dreamed of being fat. For them, in many ages and cultures, it was a sign of health, wealth and even beauty.

Today, getting fat is easy. Good food is plentiful in industrialized countries, and our physical activity is lower than the human race has ever known. The result is the simple arithmetic of calories: middle age spread, chronic obesity, diabetes or even heart problems. For the first time in history, some of us are now beginning to ask: "How can we eat less?" This means fighting nature. Like the wild goose, overeating is part of the survival instinct we have inherited from our ancestors. But heredity is unpredictable. Some of us are born with ten times as many fat cells as others: if we have few fat cells, we will never look fat however much we eat. There are also other factors. Our work might be active or sedentary. And we certainly need to eat differently if we live on the Equator or in the Arctic. So our individual ideal diet depends on who we are, what we do, and where we live. It also depends on how old we are, and the diet we need for growth at the age of 15 will certainly make us fat when we are 40!

To control our weight, we can cut down on calories by eating half as much. But at the same time we also halve all of the other essential nutrients like vitamins and minerals, and may not eat enough of them for good health. So cutting out certain foods, or simply eating less, may not always be the best answer.

"Pâté de foie gras" was the favourite food of Alaric II, King of the Visigoths. From the Middle Ages, we could savour the finesse of foie gras mixed with truffles, a speciality from Perigueux in France. The Bohemian Jews were also great goose breeders. They made a goose liver paste, and the gypsies continued this tradition.

The Alsace won its reputation for foie gras, when Louis XVI sold a plot of land to the Alsatian Governor. The price was... a goose liver pâté!

At the time of the French Revolution, the infamous Casanova sang the praises of the pâtés of Perigueux. These were made by a certain Mr. Noël, who exported them to America.

We have eaten foie gras with or without truffles, as a pâté, a paste, a parfait, a galantine or a mousse. Whichever way we have eaten it, it has always been a symbol of the lofty heights of the gastronomic arts.

Research in food science and nutrition has provided us with two ways to help control our weight safely. First, through "light" food products, where calories have been eliminated by reducing the amount of fat or sugar, or both. And second, a new and more complete approach: adapted nutrition.

Adapted nutrition starts with the basic nutrients we get from our foods: the amino acids, fatty acids, sugars, fibres, vitamins, mineral salts, trace elements... and the calories. Then, it asks: "How much of each nutrient do we need every day? How much do we find in each food or food ingredient? What combinations of foods correspond best to our needs?" Answering these questions has led to manufacturing complete low calorie meals, as part of whole diet plans. Making low calorie foods taste like their high calorie alternatives is a technological triumph, since the fat in foods gives texture and flavour. Fooling the "automatic pilot" in our stomach, so that it thinks we have eaten a high calorie meal and stops feeling hungry, is even more of a triumph. But the main advantage of adapted nutrition is that it applies to us all. Not just the overweight, but also to athletes, pregnant women, babies, the elderly, vegetarians.

For the first time in history, we have the knowledge and the means to adapt our foods to our needs, desires, and individual lifestyles. This is one of the prospects for the 21st century.

All in good taste

Seasonings and condiments were important to us. With them, we could make our food taste exactly the way we wanted, instead of simply having to accept it the way it was. We used lemons, flavoured roots such as horse-radish, onions and garlic, as well as a variety of leaves, flowers and seeds. In ancient times, garum, nuoc-mam and mustard already filled our kitch-ens with their pervasive aromas. The Greeks made a fish seasoning called garon that they used in sauces. To do this, they marinated anchovy or mackerel guts in salt, then left them in the sun until they fermented to give a strong smelling liquid. The Romans called it garum, and used it by the gallon. It contributed much to the prosperity of the fishing trade along the Mediterranean coast, from Liguria to Andalusia. From 500 BC, millions of jars of the savoury liquid were exported. Nuoc-mam was made the same way. Literally, the name in Vietnamese meant "fish water", and we already used it many centuries ago to flavour the foods of South East Asia.

In 1830, Edmund Crosse and Thomas Blackwell bought the century old Condi-ment and Relish business in London where they both worked as apprentices. The shop was already reknowned for its specialities. But at the time, these were certainly not common foods. The spices, herbs, peppers and exotic fruits that went into them were expensive. So the tasty products were made in small quantities for an elite clientele.

London society in the 1830s was a soci-ety of leisure... of butlers, cooks and kitchen maids, of English teas and dinner parties. The food industry catered for this society. Relishes and sauces were hand made and hand bottled in the back room of the shop, and were often delivered fresh for eating the same day.

The two ''saucerers apprentices'' knew that their products added flavour and colour to any meal, so they set about offering a wider variety of choice. From France, they enlisted the services of Francatelli Qualliotti, who had been Master Chef to the Emperor Napoleon. His genius soon rewarded them with new potted meats and fish... which he duti-fully made himself... and with his famous mustard relish he called a ''piccalilli''.

Somewhere back in the misty past, we invented mustard. We made this from the seeds of the sinapi, which grew wild among the cereals we planted. We ground the black or white seeds in vinegar, and added other flavouring ingredients. The Romans made mustard with oil and honey, and the Byzantines used it in their vinaigrette sauces. Sinapi changed its name to mustard in the Middle Ages, when we began to prepared it in a partially fermented grape juice called a "must". By then, Dijon in France already had a fine reputation for its ready-to-eat mustard. But we could also buy it as a solid cake, and prepare it in our own kitchen by mixing in the vinegar ourselves.

We flavoured it with spices. Then, by the end of the Renaissance, with pepper. And in the reign of Louis XIV, with vanilla or orange flower. Whatever our tastes, mustard has always evolved to suit them.

The modern food industry caters for a society where we have less and less time. Condiments, relishes and sauces have become everyday food items, and we can now buy packaged meals that would have been a banquet only a century ago. Right out of the freezer, we can serve a complete meal hot on the table in a few minutes, as if it had come directly from the hand of a modern Qualliotti.

Leading food companies still employ Master Chefs who use their skills to invent new recipes in experimental kitchens. But the chefs are not the only experts. Their recipes are adapted by food scientists and technologists, who work out how to make the same products industrially. Food engineers build machines and factories that lock the Chef's expertise in a suitable package.

This teamwork between experts with widely differing skills is the key to success in adding relish to today's new food products.

A package deal

We domesticated the pig about seven thousand years ago, in Italy. The wild creatures came along uninvited, and ate the food scraps we threw away. We were happy, and so were they. In this strange relationship, the pig ate anything and everything, and we in turn ate the whole pig from snout to tail.

For the Egyptians, Jews and Muslims, the pig was taboo. They had their reasons: the hot climate and the flies meant that the meat quickly went bad, and was a source of parasites and diseases. The Chinese, the Romans and the Greeks, turned it into pork, and ate it without a second thought. The Romans and the Gauls stuffed the intestines to make sausages, white and black puddings, and pork pâtés. Germanic tribes smoked and salted it, and Westphalian ham became a favourite meal in Ancient Rome.

In the 4th century, Constantine the Great outlawed the sausage. He thought it led to gluttony, drunkenness and debauchery. The sausage industry went underground, and the sausage survived. After all, it was almost the perfect food. We could not only eat the stuffing, but also the sausage casing, namely, the package in which it was wrapped.

Edible packaging dates back further than the sausage. Nature showed us the way. The skins of many fruits are edible. Yet, they do the same job as the package around an industrial food product.

Our ancestors imitated nature by wrapping food in leaves. Modern packaging technology follows the same principles, using materials which biodegrade or which can be recycled. The main job of the package is to keep the food safe to eat, and fresh. So it must keep out microbes and insects, and also water, oxygen and light. It also has to be solid to protect the food against rough handling. Each food needs a different type of protection, but all packages must be in convenient sizes and shapes for shopping and storage. The label identifies the product, gives instructions for preparing it, and lists the ingredients. Finally, the package must be easy to open: for example, engineers in bottling factories finely adjust the machines that screw on the bottle caps. Too loose means that dirt can get in, and too tight means that we cannot open it!

In fact, today's packaging engineers work miracles every day. And for tomorrow, their packages will offer even more. They will have a built in warning indicator to tell us when the product they contain has not been stored correctly.

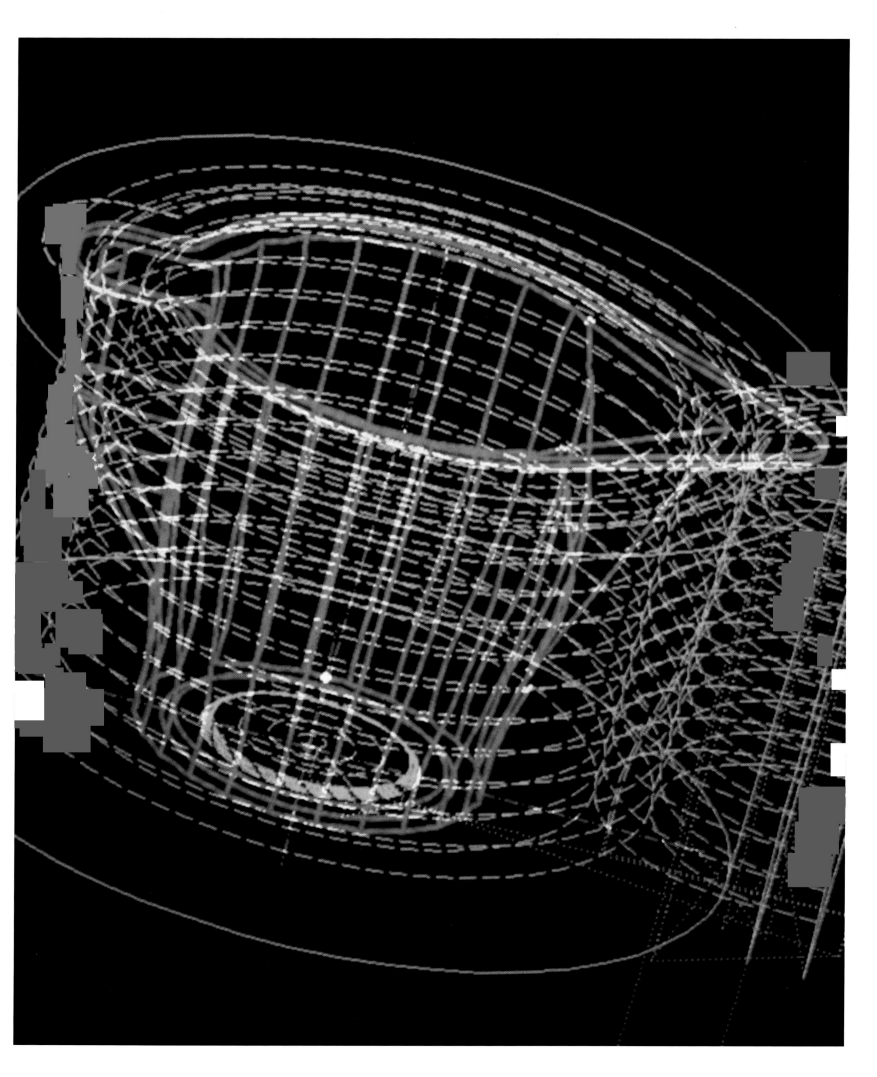

We may argue about the origins of the human race on earth. How and when we got here. Where we came from. In this argument, one thing is certain. Our food has been on earth at least as long as we have.

For millions of years, we have co-evolved along with the foods we have eaten. Each has shaped the other in a natural biological equilibrium, which still is, and will always be, one of the fundamental secrets of life.

How to increase food production? How to prevent food from going bad? How to make it taste better? Or make it more nutritious? Or more convenient? We tend to think that such questions belong to the modern world. Yet, throughout history, our ancestors have had the same problems.

Driven by the survival instinct, ingenious individuals have discovered empirical solutions. Their traditional methods... often thousands of years old... still form the basis of today's food industry, except that they have slowly been improved and optimized as each successive generation has added new knowledge.

The food industry in any era is thus the simple extension of the fight for survival which still goes on today. Its history is an intensely human story, because at the same time, it is the natural history of mankind. With our 20th century lifestyle of town and city dwelling, nature has become something we observe, and we can even forget that we are a part of it. This lack of awareness of nature has its consequences in our approach to food.

For example, the unfounded belief that industrially processed foods, manufactured in food factories, are non-natural or even synthetic.

In fact, the food processing industry does not ''manufacture'' foods at all. It simply transforms natural raw food materials... the fruits, vegetables, cereals, milk, meat and fish coming from the fields, farms, orchards and oceans... into finished food products. Packaged, and ready for use.

Not all of nature is good. So the food industry uses more and more selective processing methods. These find the balance between preserving desirable natural qualities of foods, like flavour, colour and nutritional value, and at the same time, eliminating undesirable natural properties such as the ''bugs'' which cause food spoilage and food poisoning.

Over the centuries, the food industry has slowly developed from a cottage trade to an international food chain. The chain starts with farming and fishing, then goes on to processing and packaging in food factories, and distributing finished food products to shops and supermarkets. It also includes manufacturing domestic ovens, refrigerators and many other kitchen appliances used to prepare and serve food.

Two basic concepts govern the food chain. Quality and Safety! These concepts are found in historic phrases such as: ''A meal fit for a King''. They imply that a food, whatever its cost, whatever its nature, contributes positively to health and well-being, and gives pleasure in eating. Following these principles, the products of the food industry have never been better nor safer than they are today.

Yet, even for the modern food industry, there are still problems to be solved. Only two hundred years ago, simply getting enough to eat was the story all around the world. Today, in the parts of the world where hunger is still a harsh reality, starting up local food industries is a part of the answer. So for many decades, leading food companies have been helping developing countries by providing technical aid in food production, food processing and preservation.

Looking towards the future, we can expect to see the same pattern as in our two million year story of the past. There will be new food problems for the world, and there will be new solutions. The food industry will continue to evolve in a parallel symbiosis with man to meet our needs and desires. The product of the food industry, in any age, is life, and every food item we buy will continue to be a slice of biological energy that keeps us alive and in good health.

There can be no sudden changes, like the mass production of food concentrates in capsules, pills and potions, force-fed from faceless automatic dispensers. Such visions of gastronomic disaster belong behind the kitchen doors of science fiction.

Instead, the products offered by the food industry of the 21st century will come from a normal and natural development of the products of today. Certainly, they will include the major advances in nutritional knowledge and food science achieved during the 20th century. But they will still be made to ''look good, taste good, and do us good'', following the now established industrial principles of Quantity and Convenience. Of Quality and Safety. Of Pleasure in Eating.

Authors	Maguelonne Toussaint-Samat Renaud Alberny Ian Horman under the direction of Rémy Montavon
Translation	Alexander Jennings
Design and artistic direction	Yves Racheter Peter Scholl
Iconographic research	Patrick Jézéquel Erich Lessing
Photolithography	Ast & Jakob, Berne, Switzerland
Printing	Jean Genoud, Lausanne, Switzerland
Binding	Mayer & Soutter, Renens, Switzerland
Production	NESTEC LTD., Visual Communications-CI

The authors would like to thank the many NESTLÉ
experts in food science, technology and engineering,
whose interest and personal involvement in this book
have helped make it what it is. Without their detailed
knowledge, experience and know-how, much
of it not recorded in books, the modern aspects
of the food industry could not have been presented.